SHE'S LOSING IT!

Go for your goals!

Yvore Traygott

SHE'S LOSING IT!

*A quirky little memoir about weight loss,
bodybuilding, and dealing with small children*

By Lisa A. Traugott

Lisa A. Traugott is the author and illustrator of *Mind Your Manners Minnie Monster*, which earned her a Mom's Choice Award, and the blog *She's Losing It!* She is also a National Academy of Sports Medicine Certified Personal Trainer and amateur bodybuilder.

Austin, Texas
© 2014 by Lisa A. Traugott

Some sections of the book were originally published online as blog posts at ShesLosingIt.net, 2013, 2012.

Cover photo and headshots by Caroline Poe Photography.
Back cover photo by ION Studios.

ISBN-13: 978-0-9833441-2-4

Acknowledgements

Thank you, Henri, for supporting all my crazy notions, and letting people peek in on the toughest years of our marriage. I'm glad we made it through even stronger. I love you.

Rylee and Little Henry, I love you both. You make me proud.

Regina—If it weren't for our conversation in November, I don't think I ever could have done this. Thank you.

Daniel—Thanks for helping me get my mojo back.

Mom, Dennis, Meghan, Jenny, Serena, Deirdre, Obidia, Henry Sr., Cindy, Bernie & Duda, Bob, Mona & Robert, Brenda & Gayle, and all my Gym Rat buddies, especially the ladies of Mel's Machines—Thanks for cheering me on and reading my blog.

Jamie—Thank you for turning my blog into a book! Who knew?

Caroline Poe—Thank you for taking such beautiful pictures.

Everyone who reads my blog—Thank you for reading and all your encouragement. I started writing for myself; now I'm writing for us.

And a Quick Little Note

First, hey, thanks for buying my book! I hope you like it! Second, if you've been following my blog for a while, you will note that the timeline for this book is a little off. All the events in this story happened over the course of ten months working with my trainer, Daniel Rufini. I ended up doing two bodybuilding competitions during that time. For the sake of better story flow, my editor and I decided to compress the events into the timeline of the first competition because all the weight loss and most of the mental block breakthroughs happened during that time frame.

That said, a few significant things happened during my second show that I felt should be included in the story. For example, my high school reunion happened in October, which was one month away from my second show, but in this book it appears in May, one month before my first show.

Real life is seldom as tidy as the timeline in a book, but I figured you would probably be more interested in a well-paced story than strict adherence to a calendar. Also, as this is an edited version of my life, I changed some details and occasionally people's names to protect their privacy. On the upside, now I get to write something fancy under the title, like, "Based on a True Story," which sounds pretty official, huh? Anyway, I hope you enjoy the ride, and will maybe consider giving bodybuilding a try.

DEAR FORMER ME: PART I

Dear Former Me,

My heart aches watching you sobbing in your car at Rylee's nursery school last November, tears spilling over your fingers and wetting the steering wheel you were gripping so tightly.

Of course you were crying—your life was a mess: 50 pounds overweight, your marriage on the rocks, business failing, stressed over the kids. The world was collapsing around you and you felt so lost and alone. Well, I want to tell you a few things. First, *it gets better.* Your marriage is strong again. You are in the best shape of your life. The business finally made a profit last month and the kids are just fine . . .

BLOGGER CHALLENGE:
HOW HAVE YOU CHANGED IN THE PAST 2 YEARS

In the beginning of 2009, I had a road map for life. After the birth of our second child, my husband and I quit our jobs, moved from California to Texas, and became landlords of a 27-unit apartment building, just as the Great Recession got into full swing. Though my official title was CEO, my husband ran the business and I became something I had dreamed of becoming—a stay-at-home mom.

I made friends quickly with other mommies and Regina became my new best friend instantly. Our house was the biggest we could afford; we had two years' living expenses saved in the bank and life was good.

In 2010 life went to hell in a handbasket. I got lost. Turns out being a landlord is really hard, especially when you don't speak the same language as your tenants, the building is falling apart, and you blow through your life savings without a profit in sight.

Being a stay-at-home mom was way harder than I thought it would be. While I loved spending time with my children, I hated the never-ending monotony of household chores, lack of adult conversation, and not making any money.

Resentments built between my husband and me. I was mad he made all business decisions unilaterally and never helped with housework EVER. He was mad that I suddenly had a flock of friends while he was isolated at a thankless job all day and that my "down-time" was spent on chairing a fund-raiser for Rylee's nursery school instead of clipping coupons for our family.

We should have talked but it was easier to watch TV and eat chips. I gained weight. I felt like I was useless. We hurt each other in ways that only married people can do.

By November 2011, I had had enough. I was tired of being fat. I was tired of feeling marginalized. I wanted back the power I had so easily given away. I decided to shock my system and try something radical: For my birthday gift to myself, February 2012, I was going to enter a bikini competition at age 38 and size 14.

I thought female bodybuilding would just mean lifting weights and eating healthy, but that's like saying getting pregnant just means your belly gets a little bigger. It was a life-changing, jaw-dropping experience for me. Mentally, physically, sexually, emotionally—everything changed.

I never realized how many emotions were tied to my food consumption. I never realized how many lies I had told to myself to avoid facing hard truths about my life. It took a trainer to call me out on every single bullshit excuse before I broke though my own mental blocks.

Today, I'm back in the driver's seat, the roadblocks of the past in my rearview mirror. At size 1, I'm in the best shape of my life. I stand tall, proud of my body, proud of my marriage and kids, and proud of the active role I reclaimed in our family business.

I feel like Rocky. Only in 5" heels and a bikini.

Here's my story.

NOVEMBER—THE TALK

Did your doctor ever give you *The Talk*? Although not quite as embarrassing as *The Birds and the Bees Talk* of puberty, it's up there with top conversations I'd like to wipe from my memory. If you never received it, this is how it goes.

> The doctor looks over your chart. The one with *your weight* on it. And everyone knows that doctor-office scales are at least three pounds heavier than home scales. Plus, you're wearing clothes when the nurse weighs you, right? Clothes are at least 17 pounds . . .
>
> **Doctor**: How is your nutrition?
> **Lisa**: (*Uh oh. . .*) Fine . . . well, um . . . maybe I should probably be eating, you know, a little bit better.
> **Doctor**: Do you eat fruit?
> **Lisa**: I eat apples with my kids. (*Maybe I won't fail this pop quiz after all!*)
> **Doctor**: Every day?
> **Lisa**: Uh . . . no? Like maybe every other day?
> **Doctor**: You should be eating fruit every day. And vegetables?
> **Lisa**: (*Oh God!*) Um . . . do potatoes count as a vegetable?
> **Doctor**: They are carbohydrates. Any *green* vegetables?
> **Lisa**: Sometimes I eat salad . . .
> **Doctor**: Do you exercise?
> **Lisa**: Well I can't really make it to the gym, but I chase after my kids, you know, Rylee and the baby.
> **Doctor**: How old is your baby now?
> **Lisa**: Um . . . two and a half? (*I begin to flush red. Oh no. Here it comes. The Dr. Phil moment.*)
> **Doctor**: Lisa, you're overweight and it's not from the baby anymore.
> **Lisa**: I know.

I hang my head from embarrassment. I'm sitting on that cold examining room table and wearing a hideous blue robe that does not cover everything. Well, perhaps it covers most people, but not me, because the doctor has just informed me (and noted on my chart) that my BMI is 29, which is borderline *obese*. Obese? Really? It seems more like I'm just chubby.

Doctor: Have you tried a pedometer? It measures how many steps you take each day. You can wear it and aim for a higher number each day.

Oh God, I'm so out of shape he thinks all I can do is a pedometer? I thought those were only for obese people. Oh no, does he really think I'm almost obese?

SECRETS

My BFF Regina is coming over tonight with her husband and kids. We met at the nursery school orientation last year and really hit it off. She is a born and bred Texas Republican who goes hunting (Don't Mess With Texas), and I'm a Jersey girl liberal who listens to 1990s gangsta rap, but we love hearing each other's perspective on things and are in total agreement about being obsessed about our kids.

It is a very fancy nursery school—our toddlers had to take IQ tests to be accepted (IQ tests at three!). I loved this nursery school and totally drank the Kool-Aid, volunteering to be the fund-raiser chairperson and raising something like $34,000 for them. I had hoped that this would translate into a barter—I would do all their fundraising in exchange for my daughter's tuition, which would be raised to about $8,000 once she started kindergarten, which (to my math) put them ahead by $26,000, but it didn't work out. They don't do barters.

The tuition for last year was $5,000, which we could afford. But then all hell broke loose with our real estate business, the economy kept tanking, and the bills kept piling up. This year, nursery school goes five days per week, so there was a rate increase. I had to ask my mother for a loan to send Rylee to school—$6,000. And that was a *discount* because she only goes half days! Rylee is the only student in her school who leaves at lunchtime; the rest of the kids stay until 2:30 p.m. She doesn't understand why she has to leave early and sometimes cries when I take her home. I just try to distract her.

My husband, Henri, doesn't like that we borrowed the money and neither do I. My mom says I don't have to pay her back. I'm 38 years old and can't pay for nursery school.

But Regina is coming over and I can't wait! I used to see her a lot more last year because I was always at the school since I ran the fund-raiser. But since the job/tuition exchange didn't work out, Henri and I agreed I wouldn't do any volunteering. Plus, little Henry is quite a handful these days. I'm trying to get him potty trained but he's not interested.

They finally get here and the kids run amok and the adults get to drink alcohol. Yay! I've baked about three dozen chocolate chip cookies—the good kind—with lots of extra love in the form of double bags of chocolate chips and walnuts. Henri has made his famous garlic dip, which is just cream cheese and garlic salt—which doesn't sound so great, but trust me it's amazing—to go with bags of wavy potato chips. Henri and I drink rum and Cokes and Regina and Payman are going for the Jack Daniel's.

The men only last until around 1 a.m. (novices!) and then finally, *finally*, it's just Regina and me. We have a ritual for these little get-togethers. Once all the kids and men leave us alone we let loose with the cuss words.

"@#$%!$#%@!#$!!!!!!" we said, (only we used real curse words and not cute little symbols).

And then Regina really impresses me and cusses in French and Farsi. (What would @#$%! look like in Farsi and French? Probably القرف and *merde*!) She is my hero. We proceed to get tipsy and delight in the feast before us. After we get through the conversations about our kids and potty training and gossip, she talks about her work (she's a lawyer) and I touch on our business, but I'm not in the mood to stay there, so I tell her about the newest story I'm writing. It's a romance novel set in the late 1700s with the leading lady a banker's daughter and the leading man a Scottish Highlander, but he has a secret reason why he's marrying her.

But somehow in telling the story I tell my own secret: my husband and I aren't getting along. At all. I tell her about my meltdown in the school parking lot, and the tears flow freely aided by alcohol and embarrassment.

"Oh, Lisa, I'm so sorry to hear that," she says pulling me into a hug. She is crying too, but her tears are angry ones. "I have to take a minute to compartmentalize the facts that Henri is my friend, and I like him, but I can't believe he said that to you."

I talk about my weight, and how I can never seem to keep it off, but even when I am thinner we still are walking on eggshells around each other. My husband aside, I never feel totally good when I'm thin because I think people won't like me.

"What? That doesn't make any sense. Everyone wants to be the cheerleader type."

"I know it doesn't make sense, but it just seems like people are nicer to me when I'm heavier. Well, *women* are nicer to me. When I was living in New York and acting off-Broadway, I carried about twenty extra pounds. When I lost the weight I started booking more jobs. And then I moved to L.A. and got that gig on *Buffy the Vampire Slayer*. I was one hundred seven pounds. And I said to my roommate, 'OK, I'm off to my audition.' 'Good luck,' she said and then after I closed the door I heard her say, 'Skinny bitch.'"

"She was jealous."

"She was my friend, and then she wasn't. I know it's stupid, but I just want to be liked. You'd think I'd have outgrown this need in middle school but it's always there." I pull out a chip from the bag and skim it around the dip bowl.

We talk about school and college and our past relationships. "I don't know any woman who made it out of college alive," she said.

"What do you mean?"

"You know."

The fact was, I did know what she meant, and that's another reason why I never want to get too thin—I don't want the unwanted attention from guys. I'd experienced a truly horrific incident while in college, something I'd never told anyone, and didn't like thinking about.

"I'm entering a bodybuilding competition," I tell her randomly.

"What? Where is that coming from?"

"You know the new 24 Hour Fitness that opened? Well they were offering a special—three sessions for one hundred fifty dollars. I didn't tell Henri, he would just think it was a waste of money, but I took the last cash from my maternity check and paid for it. This trainer, Chris, used to work in an office and lost a ton of weight, and she said she was entering a bodybuilding competition as a challenge, so I think I'm going to do that too."

"You want to be a bodybuilder?"

"Well, she said there was a bikini division where you didn't need to have a ton of muscles, just look soft and toned. Regina, I'm tired of feeling fat; I'm tired of feeling useless; and my stupid twentieth high school reunion is coming up. I've got to do *something*."

A beam of sunlight shot in through the window and we both squinted.

"Holy shit, what time is it?"

"Five a.m.? Quick! Eat the last cookies before the kids wake up!"

We break into fits of laughter and it's the lightest I've felt in years.

CELEBRITY CIRCLE

"What on earth were you two talking about that you stayed up all night?" Henri asked. He's sitting on the couch, watching football, eating popcorn and drinking beer. We have the best popcorn ever. Two years ago I bought him an old-fashioned popcorn machine that uses coconut oil and it tastes like real movie popcorn, because we put a ton of butter and salt on it.

"Everything," I said sitting down next to him. I've been in the office, working on my novel. Whenever I'm really trying to work through something I write. I put my characters in similar circumstances but in different time periods as me and then play "what if?" games. What if the leading man pushed her too hard? What if the leading lady stopped pretending nothing was wrong? Would things get better? Worse?

I begin to eat out of his bowl. "Who's playing?"

"Patriots versus Giants."

"I hope the Giants win. Not only because they're a better team, but also so I can soothe Tom Brady after the game in a way his supermodel wife, Gisele, never could."

Without looking at me, Henri picks up a handful of popcorn and throws it at me, shaking his head. "That's your outside voice, you know."

"Hey, he's in my Celebrity Circle*."

We continue watching for a few minutes and I move a little closer and begin to kiss his neck. He shifts away a bit. "Honey, I'm watching the game."

We watch in silence.

A Victoria's Secret commercial comes on. The woman is impossibly thin and beautiful. I never cared about those ads, but I can't help but feel inferior. Henri is leaning forward, drinking his beer.

"Henri, I know what I want for Christmas."

"What?" he asked, slightly annoyed.

"Henri, my grandmother called. She wants her underwear back."

"What?" That pulled him away from the screen.

"I'm entering a bodybuilding competition. I won't be able to do it on my own; I'll need to get a personal trainer who can give me a diet. I know the diet is supposed to be really intense or something, but I don't know what they eat. I spoke to the manager and he said if I buy ten sessions they could give me a super discount and only charge me seven hundred dollars minus one hundred dollars for another side promotion, so it would only be six hundred dollars."

"Six hundred dollars? Are you nuts?"

"Hear me out. That's only sixty dollars per session. I can stretch out the sessions too. The competition—it's called Shredder, isn't that a cool name?—it's in April, so if I start the training the same week as my birthday in February, and maybe do it every other week or something, I can stretch the sessions to last until then."

He's sitting with his arms crossed over his chest, pretending to listen and subtly shaking his head 'no.' Whenever I hear someone tell me 'no' it just means I'm not explaining it right.

"Don't you want me to look hot in a bikini?"

That perked him up.

"Lisa, I used to bodybuild in my twenties and the women who did it overbuilt their arms and looked like scary gorilla women."

"That's why I'm entering the *bikini* division. See, the point is to just look toned and soft. *Like a Victoria's Secret model.*"

He is seriously considering the ramifications of that possibility.

"How did you even come up with this idea?"

"I have something to tell you."

"You already signed up for this."

"No. I took the last of my maternity check money and bought three trainer sessions and the lady, Chris, said she was going to enter the competition."

"So now you have to? And—"

"I didn't want to tell you I did the trial session because I know we're tight for money right now. But it was my money and I'd rather spend it getting healthy than just going out to Starbucks."

"How come the maternity check is *your* money but the money I make is *our* money?"

"Henri, we've been through this. I went back to work when Rylee was three months old while you got to stay home, with the occassional babysitter who did the laundry, by the way, while I worked until Henry was born. I didn't bug you about your money/my money then. Look, I don't want to fight, I just want to lose weight and look good for my reunion, and what I'm doing clearly isn't working. I ran the half marathon last year, I did the cayenne pepper lemonade cleanse, I tried Nutrisystem®, God you know I'm trying, but nothing is working, Henri."

I exhale. This isn't going like I planned.

"Victoria's Secret model, huh?" he says.

I smile.

"OK. Merry Christmas and happy birthday. And happy Valentine's Day. Seven hundred dollars? Christ."

*"Celebrity Circle" is an agreement we made up one night while watching TV. It goes like this: "In the unlikely event that we are stranded on an island with a hot celebrity, we give each other the right to totally make out with said celebrity provided their name was on the pre-approved list of celebrities. Henri's list includes Brittney Spears (but only when she's not crazy), Kate Upton and Taylor Swift, among others. We are both totally cool with this.**

If you are my mother reading this: It's a JOKE, Mom! Of course we wouldn't cheat on each other, even with a celebrity. Duh!*

***If you are Henry Cavill, aka Superman, or Tom Brady, please disregard that last note. We have a Celebrity Circle.

HOME FOR THE HOLIDAYS

The four pounds I lost while working out with Chris throughout November were easily put back on and then some by December. We're at my mom's in New Jersey and the kids are on one giant sugar high from all the chocolate and Christmas cookies. Thank God my older brother, Dennis, is keeping them occupied so I can socialize with my friends from high school that I still keep in touch with.

I had warned them that I had gained weight since the last time they saw me, but my best friend since childhood, Meghan, can't hide her surprise. She hands me her son and takes off her coat, the cold air still on it.

"Oh, Lisa, what happened?" she whispers.

"It's been a tough year."

"How much do you weigh?"

"One hundred fifty pounds," I mumble sheepishly. I'm hugging her baby, not just because he's adorable, but because I'm using him as a human blocker to hide my body from her.

She sees how upset I am. We go inside to the living room where Deirdre and her husband, David, are talking to Henri. Their daughter, Jayden, is now BFFs with my daughter, Rylee. My other friend, Jenny, is on her way.

"I'm doing a bikini competition in April," I announce.

"Wait, what?" asked Deirdre.

"This whole, 'I'm going to be healthy eventually' thing is not working out for me, so I need something specific to work toward."

"Don't bodybuilders eat boiled chicken or something?" asked David.

"I don't know. I know the diet is important, but the trainer I worked with wouldn't tell me anything about it. I'm not sure I want to train with her, though, because I'd have to compete against her and wouldn't that be weird? Do you think I'm weird for wanting to do this?"

"No. I think it's cool," said Deirdre. She used to have crazy long curly black hair, but with raising Jayden, it got to be too much and she cut it off. It looks cute.

I cut my hair off, too, only with less appealing results. Nothing really seems to make me look better these days. My pants are too tight so my mom loaned me her stretch pants with the elastic waist. I know I should buy clothes that fit me, but I don't want to. I'm 5'2" and my size 14s are getting tight. I never got rid of my maternity clothes.

"Hey, how're your book sales going?" asked Meghan.

My husband snorts.

OK, last year I wrote this children's book called *Mind Your Manners Minnie Monster* and I did the illustrations too. Everyone I showed it to said it was really good, and I should submit it to publishers, but I was too afraid of getting a rejection letter, so I decided to sell my old Mustang and use the money to self-publish. One of the moms from Rylee's nursery school did the design layout for me and set up a website. But I was so focused on breaking through that mental block of getting it published, I never considered what to do with it once it was done. I set up an Amazon account, but my book was on page 9,000. I didn't have a distributor, so I couldn't get it into libraries or bookstores. I went to this book expo in New York with Henri and these people called The Book Doctors said that the book was really good but I needed to start a blog to develop an audience. The whole "blogging" idea scared me. Who would want to read what I wrote? And what would I even write about, anyway? The one bright spot here, though, was that my book won a silver Mom's Choice Award. So I don't know how to sell anything, but at least someone other than my family said I could write. That was nice.

Meghan's baby, Cameron, is exploring the Christmas paper, which is apparently far more interesting than the gift inside. Meghan looks great. You'd never know she had a baby.

I'm eating Hershey's Kisses and Henri is watching me, mildly pissed off. I think he's calculating all the money he's about to waste on this little bikini project of mine.

That said, he also gives me my Christmas gift after everyone leaves. I'm not expecting anything other than the training sessions. I open it to discover a giant pink Victoria's Secret gym bag with pink sparkles all over it, filled with pretty undies in every size between XL and petite.

"Whatever size you are, you're too pretty to be wearing granny pants, Lisa," he said, and he kisses me.

It's two o'clock in the morning and everyone is asleep. The Christmas lights are blinking on the tree. This is the first year since my dad died that my mom put up a tree. I told her that a poinsettia plant wouldn't cut it this year; the grandkids were coming.

I used to put up the artificial tree with my dad every year. We would lay out the branches into different piles. There was red, yellow, blue or white paint on the metal tip of each branch. My mom and brother hated putting it together so they would watch football. My dad and I would talk about politics and world events. I'd tell him how I was going to be an Academy Award winning actress some day and he believed me.

As I sit on the couch, going through old photos of my father, the lights are blinking. And I'm blinking back tears.

HAPPY NEW YEAR

Part of my gym membership means I get to take free classes, so I signed up for a 5 a.m. boot camp and a Body Pump class. I am wearing my husband's T-shirt because my shirts no longer fit me and I refuse to purchase fat clothes when I know that I'm going to have a totally rockin' size 5 body in four months.

The gym is mobbed, even at 5 a.m. It makes me happy when I see I'm only mid-range heavy compared to the other people. Some women are wearing cute yoga outfits with matching hair accessories. Who does that? At 5 a.m.?

My hair is just long enough now to put in a messy ponytail. The lights in the class are super bright fluorescent and the music is really good, but I have no idea who's singing it. It occurs to me that I haven't listened to anything but kids music for the last half decade.

The warm-up consists of running from one wall to the other. That took out about one-third of the class. I run at the speed of walking, but I won't stop until I'm done. I learned how to push through that when I ran marathons before having the kids.

As I exit the class, the personal trainers begin to arrive at the desk, waiting for their clients. They all wear red shirts and black shorts or sweatpants and carry clipboards. Some trainers actually look like they could use a trainer themselves. They kind of have pot bellies. I guess even trainers eat too many holiday treats. But most are super fit and muscular.

When I go home I eat one of the leftover meals from my Nutrisystem box. It's corn flakes in a self-contained bowl. Just add milk. It doesn't really taste that good, but I lost weight when I was on the plan. But I've eaten all the good ones, so now the sucky ones like turkey hot dogs and meatloaf are the only meals left. There are a few cans of chili too. The split pea soup, surprisingly, is pretty tasty. Maybe I'll have that for lunch. I'm trying to lose some weight before I go to my first training session.

IT GETS EASIER

Later that day, it's time to leave nursery school, only my kids don't want to go home. We are in the common area with all the other well-behaved children and their ubermoms who have stopped by to have lunch with their kids.

The other children were making advanced robotics and speaking fluently in Chinese and Farsi. My kids? One was having the mother of all temper tantrums and the other was literally running in circles holding a Lego.

Bending over to try to get the one child off the floor, it began to rain Cheerios from the overstuffed (and apparently open) diaper bag on my shoulder, and my shirt flew up, exposing to the world that even though my "baby" was two years old, I am still wearing maternity pants because I can't shake the weight. My face gets redder and redder from anger and embarrassment and I yell at myself internally.

Why can't I get my act together? All the other kids don't seem to have a problem! I read the parenting books! I watched Super Nanny! Why are all the other moms so much better at this than me?

I know their success is not my failure, but in this moment in time, I feel like the most incompetent woman on the planet.

Two moms with older kids are sitting on chairs and watching me. I must look a sight. One of the moms kneels down and helps me pick up the Cheerios. She says to me kindly, "It gets easier."

Tears of gratitude filled my eyes because "easier" is something I can look forward to. Suddenly, it was instantly easier knowing that these other moms weren't judging me, they were empathizing with me.

"I'm entering a bodybuilding competition," I blurt out, for inexplicable reasons.

"Wait, what?" she asks straightening up.

"I'm going to do a bikini competition called the Texas Shredder in April."

"Lisa that's . . . awesome!"

GUN CONTROL

The murmur of the City of Angels fades in and out like a low pulsing moan. I'm on the rooftop of a 48-story high-rise. Gravel crunches beneath my five-inch heels. I'm wearing my size 4 red-suit dress, the one that matches my Mustang GT Convertible. The silence is disturbing; it's too quiet. I know he's up here somewhere, armed and dangerous.

I hear a breath, but maybe it's my own? I turn around, but not fast enough because his fingers are tangled in my blond tresses as he yanks my head back toward him. For a split second he enjoys his victory, until the pistol I pull from my garter is aimed between his crystal blue eyes.

"Don't move. Unless you can run faster than my bullet," I say, stealing the line from the song "Pumped Up Kicks" with cool authority.

My Walter Mitty moment is interrupted by a reality check. . . . I've shot off the target wire. Again.

The loud BANG! BANG! BANG! of the guns going off around me scares the living s*** out of me. I'm standing at Red's Indoor Shooting Range in Pflugerville, Texas, population 12 people, and I keep trying to remember how to hold the 9mm gun my friend Regina lent me, but I'm shaking so badly I can hardly focus.

I squeeze my eyes closed and pull the trigger (not a very effective strategy for hitting your target) and the force of the gun pushes me back. Not to brag, but I am probably the *worst* shot in Texas. The target is held up by this metal wire and I shot off the wire. Twice.

A deep voice behind me says, "Put the gun down."

Oh good! An excuse to let go of the gun! It's the man who works at the range. He towers over me and his goggles make him look even bigger. I'm assuming he's come to inform me that I'm doing it wrong.

"Is this your first time holding a gun?" he shouts over the flying bullets.

"Yes. It's my birthday gift from my friend Regina," I shout back. The earplugs make my own voice sound odd to me.

"Happy birthday. Your stance is wrong. Put your right foot forward and your left foot back. Good. Now, I know a gun is scary to you, but holding it as far away as possible from your body is not helping your aim. Pull it closer. Good. Wrap your fingers around—right. That's right. OK, now aim, breathe, shoot."

I hit the target in the middle of the head.

"All right! That was a kill shot!"

Let me back up a little here. Today is my birthday. I'm 38 years old. And despite "trying to lose weight" before my training sessions start, I'm still a size 14.

I prefer experiences to store-bought gifts because they are more memorable and I like feeling alive, especially on my birthday. I usually pick experiences that are completely terrifying to me. Last year my gift to myself was getting my first book, *Mind Your Manners Minnie Monster*, published. (Check it out: www.minniemonsters.com.)

This year I'm going to do three (3) frightening things:

1. Start a Blog I want to be a writer and all the professional writers I've met say that I really need to start writing a blog. Blogs scare me because:

- I'm not tech savvy. At all. I joined Facebook 30 seconds ago and asked, "What's a wall?"
- I'm not sure how I will find time to update my posts in a timely manner.

- I'm afraid I'll write something offensive, get flame mail, and everyone will hate me.

2. Shoot a Gun As a Jersey girl Democrat who spent ten years living in Southern California, holding a gun is about as foreign to me as eating tofu at a steak house is for a Texan.

3. Enter a Bikini Competition This actually petrifies me the most. Seriously . . . nothing screams "bikini winner!" like a 38-year-old, size 14 woman.

But guess what? I just shot a gun! And now I only have two more goals to accomplish. What could possibly be easier? Happy Birthday to Me!

THE NEW 40

I Feel Bad About My Neck: And Other Thoughts on Being a Woman by Nora Ephron goes off on books that say it's great to be old. According to Nora's book, when I turn 43, gravity will grab hold of my neck skin and not let go.

But that kind of makes sense, because everyone knows a woman has her midlife crisis when she hits her 40s. Being an overachiever, I decide to have my midlife crisis now, at age 38, when I discover that I have already been over-the-hill for three years without knowing it.

Remember I told you that I trained with Chris last November and she's entering a bodybuilding competition? I ask her about the different divisions and she tells me the categories for women are sorted by height and age. The "Masters" division is for older women.

"So, that's for like, what, forty- to forty-five-year-olds?" I ask.

"Thirty-five."

"*Thirty-five?* Really?"

That couldn't possibly be right. But now that I'm actually going to enter the competition, I look online and she was indeed correct. Age 35 = senior citizen. This must be a bodybuilding fluke. But then I switch over to Yahoo! and there is an article about a cougar cruise and it says the women on board are between 35 and 72.

When did this happen? I thought 30 was the new 20. How, then, could 35 be the new 40? I'm only 38. *I'm not ready for my midlife crisis yet!* And while we're at it, when did size 8 become fat? Oh, who am I kidding . . . If I were a size 8 right now, I would dance around naked in my living room.

If I were a man, this would be much easier. A man going through a midlife crisis has two options:

- Buy a new sports car.
- Boink a 19-year-old barista from Starbucks.

Women, on the other hand, have three options:

- Grow old gracefully.
- Have an "oops" baby.
- Get the Mommy Special: breast implants and a tummy tuck.

Regarding "grow old gracefully"—ARE YOU KIDDING ME?

So that leaves me the "oops" baby or plastic surgery options. My problems with the "oops" baby option are that: (a) the kids would outnumber us, and (b) I would have a midlife crisis reminder living with me for the next two decades. That leaves plastic surgery; however, the only knife I can afford to go under is the plastic one that came with my kids' Play-Doh set.

So I make a new option: bodybuilding.

That night I discuss this very serious matter with my husband, Henri.

"When did thirty-five become the new forty? And how come men don't have *their* midlife crisis until fifty? Men don't live to be one hundred. Your midlife crisis should be at forty, mine should be at forty-three and a half."

"Uh huh." He totally is not paying attention to me.

"I told a woman in the sauna at 24 Hour Fitness that I just turned thirty-eight and she said, 'You're going to love your forties.' I know she was being nice, but I'm still loving my thirties, damn it! Don't get me wrong, I know that everyone gets older, I just didn't think it would happen to me personally."

"When you sign up for a trainer, make sure to tell the person that you don't want to bulk up."

Is he listening to me at all?

"I'm not going to bulk up. I'm doing the bikini competition . . . for old people. Hey."

"Hey what?"

"Did you know I've been over-the-hill for three years and didn't even know it? I guess ignorance is bliss, but still . . ."

"You think that's old, try turning fifty."

For those of you doing the math now, he's 11-1/2 years older than me. And for those of you right now saying, "Gee, Lisa, you married your dad," I'd like you to know two things: (1) My husband's personality is the polar opposite of my father's. This is a verifiable fact anyone will confirm who has met both men. (2) My husband totally lied about his age before we started dating. Here's how that went down.

Up until Henri, just about everyone I dated was within my age range by about three years, give or take. When we went out on our first date, it was obvious that Henri was older than me, but I wasn't sure by how much, so I asked him.

"Henri, how old are you?"

"How old do you think I am?"

"I don't know, tell me."

"Guess."

I was 25 at the time. I knew he was definitely in his 30s. But he was very fit from surfing (we both lived in California), he had all his hair and none were gray (a plus), and he wore Abercrombie & Fitch all the time (I'll forgive him for that).

"Thirty-two?"

"You are such a good guesser!" he cooed.

All right, seven years was a pretty big stretch, but we were both adults, and once you're out of school, age doesn't really matter. But as we went on more dates some of the things he was saying didn't add up. Like how he said he and his sister, Cindy, were three years apart and then a few weeks later mentioned it was her 40th birthday. Now, I'm not so good with math, but I did know that 32+3 did not equal 40.

"I'm so busted," he laughed.

"How old are you really?"

"Thirty-seven."

I reached into his pocket.

"What are you doing?"

"Checking your driver's license." Indeed, he was 37. "I can't believe you lied to me!" I laughed, after I punched him in the arm.

"I never lied."

"You told me I guessed right!"

"I said you were a good guesser. I never said you were right."

I'm shaking my head now, with my arms across my chest. I'm actually pretty pissed.

He moves a lock of my hair behind my ear. "Would you have dated me if you knew my real age?"

"No!"

"Well, then, I'm glad I lied, because I really like you, Lisa."

And now he's my husband, lying next to me. And for the first time today, I feel young.

CLAN OF THE GYM RAT

In high school sociology class we had to read *Clan of the Cave Bear* and dissect the various social mores of the clan. We also had to pick a clique within our school to study and discover the rules of how their tribe worked. High school is filled with factions: jocks, geeks, drama club, druggies, outcasts, sluts, lone wolves, mean girls, etc., etc. It was a fascinating assignment and I never really looked at social circles the same way again.

In the adult world we name these tribal rules "corporate culture" and "social climbing." The gym is no different. People who work out all the time are the tribal elites. I refer to them as the Gym Rats. Gym Rats only respect two things: (1) a fit body, (2) evidence of an improved body.

As a newbie to the gym, you can immediately identify the Gym Rats because they are (1) incredibly ripped, and (2) will completely ignore you if your fitness level is less than theirs.

Each January a fresh crop of newbies enter the tribal gyms in an effort to lose weight and follow through with their New Year's Resolutions. Gym Rats are vaguely annoyed by this annual ritual because it means the parking lot is crowded and they have to wait for their favorite equipment. But they will give a cursory glance at the newbies and place bets on how long each will last.

People who really don't want to be at the gym are the first victims in the evolutionary process. You can tell they won't last past January 5th because they are the ones who are reading books on the treadmill. Another general tell-tale sign of someone about to get voted off the island is the person who wears jeans and flip-flops to work out in.

By mid-January the crowds have thinned and you begin to recognize other people who consistently take fitness classes with you. You mentally note who is fatter, thinner and the same size as you so you can begin to compare your fitness progress.

People who know they need help will hire a personal trainer. People who are serious about getting healthy show enthusiasm trying to keep step as their trainer moves from one machine to the next. (It seems like trainers enjoy running from one area of the gym to the next just to see how winded they can get their clients.) The people who just aren't into it can be spotted easily too. They are the ones who show up late to their sessions and seem to talk more than train, probably about why it's too hard for them to train.

Do-It-Yourselfers will stand behind people lifting dumbbells and try to mimic the exercises being done. But being newbies, their form will be completely wrong and the Gym Rat will try very hard to not laugh at them. (After all, the newbie is trying, and this is respected by the Gym Rat . . . subject to certain provisions.)

The Gym Rat will give a perfunctory nod of approval to newbies showing up to the gym consistently at 5 a.m. But if the newbie's body has not improved within a one-month time frame all respect is lost, because a Gym Rat knows that the newbie might be exercising but is not eating "clean," which is why the newbie is still fat.

Right now I'm trying the Do-It-Yourself thing, but soon I will have a trainer. And some weird bodybuilder diet. And maybe one day I'll be a Gym Rat?

SAUNA TALK—PART 1

I'm wrapped in one of the towels they have at the front desk. They used to have all the towels in the locker rooms, but now they have them at the reception desk for some reason. Anyway, it doesn't close. I'm wearing my black tankini, which looks stupid because it opens at the worst place possible —my pot belly. But I don't want to wear my maternity bathing suit anymore (also a tankini), so I just try to cover myself and keep the open section of the towel down my side.

I move to the dry sauna, but only because the steam sauna is broken. I prefer the steam sauna because no one can see you, really, and you don't talk to anyone. People just breathe deeply and get a warm steam bath.

The dry sauna is trickier. Everyone sees each other sweating, and people tend to talk. I tell myself that everyone is thinking about their own stomach and not mine, but it doesn't really make me feel better. I take my hair out of the ponytail in an attempt to make myself look more attractive.

There are two men and a woman talking. They all look around my age, and no one is particularly svelte, so I feel better. They are talking about pigs.

Yes, pigs. This is Pflugerville, Texas after all.

Well, apparently pigs are a real problem for farmers. This guy, James, is a farmer and has two daughters who like horseback riding, and I got an entire education about pigs snouting for food, and the good spots to go hunting for them.

"I shot a gun for my birthday!" I said, wanting to participate in the conversation.

"What kind?"

"A little one."

"Colt 45 Magnum?"

"A little one . . . It was cool." *I hate it when I'm lame.*

They went back to talking about pigs.

THE CHRIS DILEMMA

I still havn't signed up for my training sessions yet because I'm stressing over picking my trainer for the competition. Not in an analytical way, as my husband would be, but in an "I hope I haven't offended you" sort of way. See, Chris is the trainer who told me about the Shredder bikini competition in November. She helped jump-start my excitement to get in shape again before the holidays. But now that it's time to commit to a long-term trainer, I want to go to someone else and this makes me feel uncomfortable.

"I don't understand your dilemma," says Regina over breakfast. Thursday is our day to hang out since our daughters are in nursery school together and our sons are in a two-hour Spanish immersion program once a week. We were going to use this two-hour time slot to exercise around Lady Bird Lake, but chitchatting over ham and cheese omelets with hash browns and buttery biscuits at Waterloo seemed a much more prudent use of our time. This will be our last breakfast together though, because her son starts nursery school next week since he just turned three.

"Well, I don't know if she makes a commission off the training sessions, so I feel bad she told me about the competition and then I switch to a different trainer on her. She'll probably be offended. But if she's in the bikini competition, too, I don't want to be trained by her because that would make me feel weird competing against her. Either way, I'll have to see her all the time at the gym and I just know it's going to be awkward."

Regina rolls her eyes at me. She knows I have issues with wanting people's approval. She exudes confidence and doesn't have that whole "I want to be liked" complex like I do. She talks me down off my nervousness.

"Lisa, who cares what she thinks? You are paying for a service. Is this woman a bodybuilder?"

"No. This is her first competition."

"Well, she was fine at getting you started on weight loss. Now you need someone who specializes in bodybuilding, since that's what you're training for."

"You're right."

"I know," she smiles, taking a bite of her biscuit.

Ah, thank God for Regina.

MEET YOUR TRAINER

I pay for the pack of training sessions (finally!) and set up my first session for 2 p.m. on February 7. The manager is about nine feet tall and types in my credit card information.

"So you want to do a competition?" He sounds pleasant, but I can tell he's thinking I'm crazy.

"Yeah, when you're middle aged and borderline obese is there really a better time to enter a bikini competition?" He looks at me oddly. Not everyone gets my sense of humor.

"My twentieth high school reunion is coming up."

If I were writing his dialogue, his line would be something like, "Twentieth reunion!?! No way! You look like you graduated yesterday!"

What he actually said was, "Oh?" He's still typing. "Are you going to continue with Chris?"

"Um . . . Chris was great. She's a really good trainer. I just don't want to compete against her. Is that weird?" *Oh God, now I'm asking for validation from the 24 Hour Fitness manager.*

"I think it would be fine. She's helping you reach your fitness goals after all, but you need to be comfortable. Do you have someone in mind?"

"Someone who is a bodybuilder, I guess."

"My roommate, Daniel, is a bodybuilder. I think he'll be great for you."

"And he'll help me with the diet? I heard that's important."

"Yes." He hands me my card and my receipt, wishes me a happy birthday and I begin to head out the door.

"Oh, wait. So who's my trainer? What does he look like?"

The manager walks me over to the training section of the gym.

Daniel, my new trainer, is with a client. In a nutshell, he is your typical 24 Hour Fitness trainer: tall, dark, good looking, and very fit. He also looks like he graduated college about 12 minutes ago. My stomach clenches.

Oh, this is going to be a mistake! Chris was older than me; she had had C-sections too; used to work in corporate America like me; and she absolutely understood what I was going through. This kid is going to make me run laps around the gym!

Daniel looks up, sensing he is being watched. I smile and wave. He waves back, a befuddled expression on his face. The manager and I laugh at his confusion.

What have I just gotten myself into?

So You Want To Do A Competition

It's 2 p.m. on February 7, my first training session with Daniel. I cajole both children into Kids' Club and say a silent prayer that I don't get paged in the middle of the session. Rylee is fine—she's used to school—but little Henry is permanently attached to my hip, and as I leave him in the middle of the toy land, I hear him repeating a mantra: "Oh no. Oh no. Oh no. " The babysitter assures me he will be fine.

Daniel is sitting at the training desk. Chris is in the training area with another client. She is not looking at me, but I still feel pangs of guilt. "So you want to do a bodybuilding competition," he says, smiling.

"Yes. Texas Shredder. My husband wants me to reiterate that I don't want to look like a scary gorilla woman, just very good in a bikini." Some other trainer holding a stability ball walks by with a client and sniggers at the comment. *Did I ask something stupid?*

"You won't look like a gorilla woman."

"Oh good," I mumble.

"Have you ever done a competition before?"

"Never."

"Why do you want to do this?" he inquires, his head tilted to the side.

"Well, my high school reunion is coming up in the fall and I seem to do better when I'm training for something specific. Just saying, 'I want to be healthy forever' is not really working for me."

"Which competition did you want to enter?"

"The Texas Shredder in April."

"No offense, but the other girls have had a huge head start on their training and you're not going to be ready for Shredder."

Ouch. I laugh, though. At least he's honest and not blowing smoke up my size 14 ass. I don't want to go onstage and look ridiculous.

"There's a competition in June called the Adela Garcia Classic. That's the one I want you to sign up for. But before you do that, you need to do some research. You need to know what you're getting yourself into." He writes down some things on a piece of paper that mean nothing to me. NPC. Adela Garcia. Figure posing. "These are some websites I want you to check out. Watch YouTube videos of female bodybuilding competitions, specifically bikini and figure. Next time we meet, tell me what you think and if you still want to do this."

Well, now I'm nervous. What *am* I getting myself into?

BODYBUILDING 101

So after putting the kids to bed that night, I do extensive research (I read wikipedia.org) and discover the following things:

- Bodybuilding is changing the physique of your body through strength training and diet.
- It is a niche sport. To put it in perspective, a marathon is a sport where the athletes train for months to run 26.2 miles. The Boston Marathon has over 20,000 runners. The New York City Marathon has 30,000 runners. In comparison, the Texas Shredder, one of the biggest amateur bodybuilding competitions in Austin, has about 300 competitors. Fewer than 2% of the human population attempts this sport, even on an amateur level.
- Modern bodybuilding was started in the 1880s by some German guy who moved to England named Eugen Sandow. In the past, there were "strong men" who used to lift heavy items for audiences, but

Eugen was the first guy to do poses showing off his muscles during a stage show. The crowd went wild, and a new sport was born.

- But is bodybuilding really a sport? There seems to be controversy over this. Powerlifting is a sport based on strength, whereas bodybuilding is a cosmetic sport, meaning strength is a nice benefit, but the important part is that your muscles look plumb, well-defined and symmetrical. So, a powerlifter dude says, "Hey! Look at me! Look how strong I am!" whereas a bodybuilder dude says, "Hey! Look at me! Look how strong I *look*!"

I knew Arnold Schwarzenegger was a bodybuilder (doesn't everyone?), but never heard of anyone else. Or so I thought! Lou Ferrigno, aka The Incredible Hulk, was a bodybuilder. Who knew? And you know who also started as a bodybuilder? Sean Connery, aka 007 James Bond. He was in the 1950 Mr. Universe contest, which got him noticed for more acting roles.

Name-dropping time—I actually met Arnold Schwarzenegger once. It was at one of his 50th-birthday fund-raisers in San Diego for some proposition he was trying to pass in the state legislature. Other people paid like $10,000 for a formal picture with him; I just photo bombed him and smiled while my husband took a pic with his phone. Arnold probably took pity on me because I looked pregnant. (I took pity on myself because I actually wasn't pregnant, just chubby. Some women are apple-shaped, others are pear-shaped. My shape? Bun-in-the-oven.) But I digress . . .

Who is Adela Garcia and why should I enter her competition? Whoa! She won the Ms. Olympia Fitness seven times! I watched her YouTube video and was amazed watching her weave gymnastic moves between things like one-handed push-ups. OK, now I know that the fitness division is *totally* out of my league, but at least I know why the local competition is named after her. Her competition (also called a *show*) follows NPC rules. NPC is the National Physique Committee, and they put on a ton of amateur bodybuilding competitions all year long. I had no idea that bodybuilding was so established.

And then there is natural bodybuilding (no steroids) versus standard bodybuilding (don't ask/don't tell).

But most of the information online seems to be about men. What about the women? Do they all look like dudes? Hardly! Except for those crazy muscular-looking women in the YouTube videos titled "Open Women's

Bodybuilding." I'm thinking, *To each her own—but I want to be strong yet still look feminine.*

Female bodybuilding competitions have several subdivisions, but Figure, Fitness, and Bikini are the main ones. Figure requires some serious muscle tone. This division has women with bikinis that crisscross in the back. They do four poses: face front, 1/4 turn to the right, face back, and 1/4 turn to the other side before returning to front pose. These women look beautiful. Strong, confident, poised.

Fitness requires a routine along the lines of what gymnasts do (I do gymnastics *never*).

And then there's Bikini . . . Bikini division means looking really good in a bathing suit and having some serious swagger, because you have to walk in said bikini wearing 5" heels and look like you mean it. Bikini is like the entry level for women's bodybuilding. The women have great muscle tone but still look soft and feminine. (Teeny tiny bikinis and 5" heels will do that.) And the poses are sexy and fun.

What strikes me the most while doing this research is how at ease all these women seem in their bodies. At 50 pounds overweight, I just can't even imagine myself standing onstage *in a bikini*(!!!), let alone being sassy and flirty. But I know I want to be confident again, and maybe this is the way?

MEASUREMENTS AND WEIGH-IN #1

"Well, what do you think about bodybuilding?" Daniel asks me at our next training session.

"I don't know," I say, shaking my head. "I don't think I could ever have that many people look at me in a bikini." I'm wearing my sweatpants that feel too tight and a ratty old green T-shirt from Walmart that covers my flabby arms.

"That's 'cause you don't like your body right now. After you put in hard work, trust me, you're going to want people to look at you."

I half smile. I'm looking down, playing with some paper at the trainer's desk. I feel like I'm jumping off a cliff into the unknown. *I'll never be able to do this*, I think.

I guess my face is wearing my thoughts because he smiles and says, "Lisa, you're going to be amazed by what you're going to accomplish in one month. You won't recognize your body. Let's take your measurements." He picks up his clipboard and begins to walk away. I take a deep breath and follow him. *Let the bodybuilding begin.*

Ah, measurements. What fun humiliation! I curse myself for eating that second (OK, third) piece of ice cream cake last night, but I had to finish it, didn't I? I'm sure cake won't be on the diet going forward.

"So what did you weigh when you trained with Chris?" he asks nonchalantly.

Oh man. I knew all the trainers talk. I feel myself blush.

"I don't know. She was a really good trainer. Really good. I just feel weird about training with someone who is going to compete against me."

I take off my shoes and step on the scale—146 pounds. Damn birthday cake. At least it's not the 150 pounds it was on New Year's Day. Progress. I like it.

"So what do you do?" he asks, taking out the white instrument that measures your body fat. This tool was created by a direct descendent of the Head Torturer for the Spanish Inquisition.

"My husband and I own an apartment building. He runs it and I do the bookkeeping and take care of the kids. The units are really big and we fully remodeled most of them."

"My roommate and I just signed a new lease. Too bad I didn't know about your building. Put your arm behind your back." He pinches away and writes down the numbers.

"Well, we're open to bartering training sessions for rent, and my husband wants to eventually get in shape, too. So maybe next year when your lease is done you can check our building out. We also pay for referrals." He pinches my flabby stomach, waist, and legs. I want to crawl in a hole and die.

"My girlfriend is looking for an apartment."

"Oh? Is she a trainer too? Maybe I could work a barter with her."

"Uh . . . no. She's not a trainer."

Oops. Knowing that I already switched trainers ("the Chris Dilemma"), suggesting to my new trainer (Daniel) that perhaps I might switch *again* with his girlfriend (don't even know her name) before we even had our first session was probably not the wisest comment to make, but sometimes there is no filter between my brain and mouth.

I recover via switching subjects. "I'm also a writer. I wrote a children's book that won a Mom's Choice Award. It's called *Mind Your Manners Minnie Monster*. I did the illustrations too."

"Wow. That's cool. My nephew could probably use a book like that."

"I'll bring one for him next time."

He does some calculations. "You're at twenty-nine percent body fat. To be in the competition you need to be at ten to eleven percent. You weigh one hundred forty-six pounds. You're goal should be one hundred fourteen to one hundred twenty-five pounds."

"I used to be an actress. I weighed one hundred seven pounds then."

"That's too thin. You need to be one hundred fourteen to one hundred twenty-five pounds. But I don't want you to focus on the weight. I'm more concerned with lean body mass. You females get too caught up with the weight part," he chuckles.

Well that's because weight is how "we females" get judged, Alpha Male, I think to myself.

He's reading my mind again.

"Seriously, don't worry about your weight. I'll get you to your goal." And then he says what would become his own mantra during this entire process. *"Just trust me."*

FOOD JOURNAL

My husband has been bugging me for years to keep a food journal. "It will help keep your diet on track," he says. "You probably don't even know what you're eating," he adds.

"OK, honey," I always reply.

I will never keep a food journal.

"This is the online food journal you'll be keeping," says Daniel. Oh great. He and my husband are in cahoots.

"You'll need to update it every day. There's a diet in there, but that's not what I want you to follow. I'll give you a special diet for bodybuilding. For now, I just want you to log in what you're eating normally. The most important thing for a bodybuilding competition is to eat clean."

"Eating clean" in the bodybuilding world means sticking religiously to the meal plan. No junk food, no alcohol, no deviations. Period. Little did I know at the time that the stupid food journal would become the bane of my existence.

But I give it the ol' college try and log in my food. Holy hell! I was consuming like 2,200 calories, and half of it was just eating my kids' leftovers.

Who knew?

BLOGGER BIRTH

Since Valentine's Day is coming up, the Pflugerville Library is hosting a discussion with three local romance novelists. Henri is watching the kids so I can go for an hour. I arrive to find a table filled with every kind of chocolate deliciousness you can imagine. Cupcakes, brownies, chocolate hearts, you get the idea. 'Cause nothing says "love and romance" like chocolate.

But I stay strong. I don't want to have to write in "cupcakes" in my food journal, because that would be wrong. Right?

Each woman speaks about her book and the path she took to get it published, and then we audience members get to talk to each of them one-on-one to practice pitching our own books, or whatever we want to talk about, really.

So I tell the author with the red hair my romance novel pitch. She's actually pretty into it, which is cool, because she didn't seem that into the other two pitches before me. My problem is that the Scottish book keeps getting more and more complicated plot lines, and even though I know how I want it to end, I don't know how to make the beginning connect to the end yet.

"You have 'The Middle of the Book Sucks Syndrome,'" she said. That sounded specific and very official.

"What's that?" I asked.

"The excitement of figuring out the beginning and the end is over and the only thing left is hard work and rewrites. But you have a really good storyline and the characters are interesting. I think you just need to practice writing more. Do you have a blog?"

"No," I say sheepishly.

"Everyone has a blog," said another author. She had short whitish gray hair and grandkids.

Shit, even grandma has a blog!

"Look, the first thing any publisher is going to do when you send them a manuscript is Google you. You need an online presence."

"I know," I said. I've been told this before. "Does it have to be about my romance novel? I'd feel weird writing kissing scenes online. I wrote a kids book, but I don't want to write a Mommy blog. I don't really feel qualified for that." *(Pretty telling statement, huh?)*

"You can write about anything you want. You just need to do it consistently. Read other blogs and books to get ideas. Writers read, and writers write. Daily. Good luck to you."

Hmm.

The librarian hands me a bag of romance novels and a bag of chocolate candies as a parting gift. I take two more bags of candies (one for each kid) and start to leave.

Then I get a brilliant idea: I'll blog about the bikini competition! I have absolutely no experience in it, so no one's expecting me to be an expert. I already started the story by signing up for training, and know it ends somehow with me looking hot in a bikini (perfect ending, if you asked me), so this whole daily blogging thing will take care of "The Middle of the Book Sucks Syndrome" for me. Perfect!

Now I just need a name for the blog.

LISA VS. DANIEL—ROUND 1 (EXERCISE CALENDAR)

Daniel has given me an exercise calendar I'm supposed to follow.

"Bodybuilders do what's known as a split. You work out different muscle groups each day allowing for rest in between. Lifting weights tear the muscles. On your rest days the muscles build themselves back stronger. That's how you grow them. Make sense?"

"Sure."

"I want you to get a little notebook. This is going to be your workout journal."

Oh great. Another journal.

"This is how I want you to write it:

　　　　Lat pulldown　　　15/15/15

40/45 /50

First you write the exercise. The top line is how many sets and reps you do."

"Reps?"

"Repetitions. You're going to pull the bar down fifteen times. You do that three times; three sets of fifteen reps. The line beneath it is the weight you're lifting. Make sense?"

I nod my head, "Yeah."

"Put the date in the top right corner, that way when you look back you can see the progress you're making. When we're not training together, I want you to follow that exercise plan. I'm going to need you to really stick with it, though, and do the muscle group on the day that I wrote on your calendar. Even if it seems heavy, you need to do what's written. You're going to need to motivate yourself."

"Well, what happens if Body Pump is doing a different muscle group?"

"Wait, what?"

"I'm taking the Body Pump class on Thursdays and the boot camp on Tuesdays."

"No, ma'am."

MA'AM? MA'AM??? I'm 38 not 60! What's up with this Southern hospitality bullshit?

"No ma'am . . . no what no?" (I know it's hard to believe after reading that display of verbal eloquence, but I actually won a divisional public speaking contest for Toastmasters once.)

"I don't want you doing those classes anymore. I don't want you over-training. Only do what I wrote on your calendar."

What the hell is over-training? Shouldn't I be training as much as I can to fit in a bikini? What are they teaching these days in personal training school?

"Um. OK. About that calendar thing. You want me to walk on the treadmill, but I think I can actually run. I used to run marathons before I had kids. Actually, some girls from the new church I'm going to are going to do the Dallas half marathon, and I was thinking I could do it with them to kind of jump-start my cardio."

"No, ma'am."

Again with the ma'am? Really?

"This is a completely different sport you're training for. The bikini competition is a very specific thing, and requires different training and different nutrition than a half marathon."

"But I really like to run." I'm totally pouting now, because since I stopped volunteering at the nursery school I'm kind of cut off from society and was looking forward to making friends with some new people.

"You can run after the competition, I promise. Just trust me."

"Um, OK Daniel."

"Here's your new meal plan. Are you excited?" He holds it just out of my reach.

"Yes, yes, yes, yes, yes, yes!!" I grab it and he laughs. "Holy crap, this is a lot of food."

OK—my meal plan can be found at the back of the book, because I asked Daniel if it was OK if I [shared it] and he said yes. But here are some disclaimers:

1. He designed this diet for me, specifically, (5'2", 146 lb., age 38) and I have no health issues beyond being overweight.
2. The diet has 1,500–1,800 calories per day, understanding that I will be working out twice per day (cardio in morning and weight training in afternoon).
3. This meal plan is written as a source of information only. The information contained within should by no means be considered a substitute for the advice of a qualified medical professional, who should always be consulted before beginning any new diet, exercise or other health program. We expressly disclaim responsibility for any adverse effects arising from the use or application of the information contained herein. (I'm not sure who the "we" are, other than me, but it sounds really official and lawyery, so Ima go with it.)

WHAT THE HELL IS QUINOA?

I'm so excited to start my meal plan! I know, right now you're thinking: It's a diet. What's so exciting about that? Well, I like *anything* that is shiny and new, even a diet. As a professional yo-yo dieter, I can tell you there are certain rituals involved with this new diet process.

The 7 Stages of Dieting

- **Stage 1—Last Hurrah**. It's a Friday. You know your new diet is going to start on Monday because all new diets start on Mondays. It's the law. So you have your last hurrah and eat everything you can get your hands on that has sugar, salt or fat in it. Now is the time to load up on chocolate, pasta and booze. And fried chicken.
- **Stage 2—Shopping.** Each new diet has its own little quirks and demands certain ingredients. For example, the cayenne pepper lemonade cleanse mandated a very specific type of maple syrup that required me to travel to three different HEBs before I found it. I probably just should have started in Whole Foods, where all cleanse ingredients go to die, but their parking lot scares me.
- **Stage 3**—Start the Diet.
- **Stage 4**—Lose Some Weight
- **Stage 5**—Cheat on the Diet
- **Stage 6**—Gain Back Weight (plus two more pounds).
- **Stage 7**—Why Didn't the Diet Work? (It must be my genetics.) Oh look! A Shiny New Diet! Let's try that one!

Repeat. For about two decades.

My birthday cake was my last hurrah. Now, since I only got the actual diet yesterday, and was just logging in my own regular meals into the food journal, I had to skip stage 2 (shopping) and go directly to stage 5 (cheating) with the earlier mentioned chocolate hearts from the Pflugerville Library. Those chocolates were my tax dollars at work.

But now that I have the actual diet, I was able to initiate stage 2 last night. I was able to find all the food at HEB except quinoa. What the hell is quinoa, besides a great word to use in Scrabble? Daniel said it was some rice type thing. Why can't I just eat white rice then?

And can we please discuss pineapples for a minute here? Daniel says I can't eat canned pineapples because they are packed in syrup and I have to buy, like, a real pineapple. Have you seen real pineapples? They have Stegosaurus armor type protection and a fern growing out the top. How am I even supposed to open the thing—with an ax?

I just finished dropping Rylee off at nursery school and run into Regina in the parking lot. Yay!

"Hey, skinny! You look like you lost weight in your face!" she said.

"I did! Just stopping cocktails helped me lose two pounds."

"Hey, let's grab some coffee."

"I can't have that," I said.

"No coffee? What's up with that?"

"He said I'm putting too much creamer and sugar in my coffee and wants me to only drink water or green tea."

I put little Henry into the car seat next to her son, Alex, and Regina drives us over to the Coffee Bean. We both order green tea and sit in the parking lot to chat. Regina has Veggie Tales playing on the DVD player strapped to the back of her car seats and the boys are content.

"How's training going?"

"Great! I have an exercise calendar, and a meal plan, and I bought a notebook to write down my splits—"

"You're doing splits? Like cheerleading splits?"

"Oh, no. Split-up muscle groups so you work them on different days. And I do cardio too. I'm supposed to take the weekends off, but I don't want to, so I went this weekend anyway. I really want to lose the weight."

"And everything was OK with the Chris situation? You think this trainer is a good fit for bodybuilding?"

"He's definitely into it. I think he's the right guy."

"See?" She's smiling as she sips her tea.

"Hey, didn't you meet with a personal trainer?"

"We joined the Y and I got a free trial session, but I don't think I'm going to go back."

"Why not?" I asked sipping my tea. It was goodish, not coffee and vanilla creamer good, but okay.

"I go there and without weighing me, or asking me anything at all about my goals or past history, or anything really, he starts me lifting weights."

"That doesn't sound right. Daniel didn't even give me the meal plan until I researched bikini competitions online and agreed I was up to the challenge."

"I know, he should have asked about my goals, right? And then partway through I was paged to go to the childcare because Alex needed to use the potty, so I was gone for twenty minutes."

I turn to my son. "Did you hear that, Henry? Alex is potty trained. You could do that too! Won't that be fun?"

"No."

I turn back to Regina. She continues.

"So by the time I get back, the session is almost over, and the trainer is annoyed with me and said something snotty like, 'I didn't think you were coming back.'"

"My trainer could beat up your trainer. Maybe you could come to my gym, and train with Daniel? It would be so much fun to have a workout partner!"

"You live in Dallas." (That's our little joke. Regina lives in Austin and I'm way out in the boonies of Pflugerville, just next to Round Rock. Austin's motto is: Keep Austin Weird. Pflugerville's motto is: . . . Between a Rock and a Weird Place.) "What's the meal plan like? I hear it's pretty intense."

"Not too bad. Mostly chicken and vegetables, but I have to buy this stuff called quinoa." (Only I pronounce it "Kin-NOAH.")

"You mean quinoa?" (Only she pronounces it "KEEN-wah.")

I blush. "Right. KEEN-wah. I have no idea where to find this stuff."

"Costco has big bags of it. It's a grain and is really delicious."

Regina cooks things. I defrost things and heat them in the microwave.

"How do you cook it?"

"Well, I do one part quinoa and two parts chicken stock and sometimes add nuts to it. Other people add cranberries too. It's so good."

"I don't think I'm supposed to add anything but water."

"Oh."

The boys laugh at something on the video. My cell rings and I jump. Shit! I forgot I was supposed to drive the checkbook to the office right after drop-off. I pick up the phone.

"WHERE ARE YOU!?! YOU WERE SUPPOSED TO BE HERE THIRTY MINUTES AGO!!" My husband is shouting and Regina is looking at me and I keep saying, "Henri, Henri, Henri, Henri," so he shuts up.

"Henri! I'm with Regina. I'm on my way."

"THE GUY IS WAITING!"

"Stop. Shouting. At. Me," I say through clenched teeth and I hang up on him. I'm mortified that Regina just overheard that.

"We better head back." Regina starts the car and we drive back to the school making awkward small talk. My phone rings again and I don't answer it. I say goodbye and get little Henry in the car and start driving to the building. My phone rings again and I light into him.

"YOU forget the checkbook, I'm doing YOU a favor by driving it down to you, and you have the nerve to yell at ME?"

"YOU'RE LATE! YOU'RE ALWAYS LATE! THE GUY IS WAITING, JUST SO YOU CAN BULLSHIT WITH REGINA!"

"YOU ALWAYS FORGET EVERYTHING! WHY DOES YOUR IRRESPONSIBILTY ALWAYS TURN INTO MY EMERGENCY? I HAVEN'T SEEN REGINA IN WEEKS AND YOU EMBARRASSED ME!" I hung up on him again. I look in the rearview mirror and see my son looking at me.

Exhaling to calm myself down, I turn on some kid songs on the CD player. I hope we're not messing up our kids with our constant fighting. Why can't we just be a normal family? The phone rings again. I turn up the music louder and just drive to the building. He's talking with a tenant.

I drop off the checkbook in the office and leave. A minute later I get a text.

"Sorry."

WELCOME

On Mondays, Wednesdays and Fridays I'm supposed to do my ab routine. Daniel had me come in yesterday between his other clients so he could quickly teach me the moves. That, in and of itself, was craziness because I don't speak text.

To explain: I'm 38. I am comfortable with email (which I started using in 1995, when I was in college) and Microsoft Office. We don't own iPhones because Henri doesn't want to pay for the two-year contract, so I have an old-school regular phone. I joined Facebook three minutes ago, my toddler is better on the computer than I am, and every day I thank God I have children because this means at least someone in the house will know how to turn on the TV for the next 18 years.

Daniel is in his early 20s, which means he's all about texting on his smart phone. Yesterday he sent me this.

9:08 a.m. Daniel: Tom we need 2 do ur abs k?

Who is Tom, and what is this new Sanskrit? So I write back (slowly).

9:08 a.m. Lisa: ????
9:09 a.m. Daniel: Can u meet tom @ 24 so I can show u abs?

Ohhhh. Tom = tomorrow. OK. I can learn text.

9:10 a.m. Lisa: That's fine. Like 10?
9:10 a.m. Daniel: Perfect. TTYL.

T-T-Y-L? That's way harder than "tomorrow." Ten-Tomorrow-You-Lisa? That makes no sense. Or maybe it means Tomorrow at Twenty-Four You're Late? But how could I even be late when it's for tomorrow? Oh f*** it, I'll just ask

9:12 a.m. Lisa: I'm an old person. What does TTYL mean?
9:12 a.m. Daniel: Talk to you later. LOL.
9:12 a.m. Daniel: LOL means Laugh out loud.

I hate being old.

He didn't charge me for the session, he just wanted to make sure I got started on them since having a hard stomach was clearly a prerequisite for entering a bikini competition. My first ab routine is to do a series of plank holds combined with crunches.

I wrote everything down in my notebook and today it's time for me to try these things on my own. I'm supposed to do this in the trainer area, where all the mats and stability balls are located, but that's in clear view of all the people on the treadmills, and honestly I don't want an audience doing these yoga moves.

So, all stealth-like, I grab a mat and stability ball and head over to the rehab area, where people with injuries stretch, and do it in the very corner where no one will see me.

No one except Daniel, apparently.

"It's a sixty-second hold."

"Huh?" He is standing next to his client, an older woman with brown hair, who is doing walking lunges.

"You stopped at forty-five. Hold for a minute." He's smiling though.

"Oh, okay."

Shit! How did he find me? So now I have to do the **whole** routine like he told me to: Front plank (hold one minute), side plank (30 seconds each side), stability ball crunches (one minute), levers aka lower-ab crunches (one minute). But it was not just holding the death poses for a minute; I had to repeat this torture three (3) times! He said I would be done with them in 15 minutes, but he is a liar, because it took me 30 minutes, since I had to keep stopping and catching my breath midway through. Also, I was using my husband's old iPod as the timer and it took me a while to find a really good song to pause on for a minute. By the end of the 30 minutes I am a hot mess and collapse on the ground because it feels nice and cool on my face.

Daniel kneels down to me after giving his client a high five.

"Planks suck," I moan.

"Welcome," he says.

LISA VS. DANIEL—ROUND 2 (LASAGNA)

I log in my code at the trainers' desk and Daniel looks through my food journal.

"Lasagna, huh?" he asks.

"Oh, that's from church group. We're going to a bible study thing at Austin Stone because they provide free child care and dinner. I would sit through a timeshare presentation for San Quinton prison if they provided free child care and dinner."

"You can't have lasagna. You need to follow the meal plan I gave you."

"I know, but I think I'm doing it wrong. I ate two cups of vegetables like you said, but the calorie count ended up being over eighteen hundred. That can't be right."

"Don't eat peas. Stick to green beans."

"Who knew peas were the Antichrist?"

"Well, now *you* know they are, so it's good you're keeping a food journal."

"Peas aside, shouldn't my calorie count be lower? Like thirteen to fifteen hundred?" *Honestly, I've been dieting for years and I know that fewer calories = skinny Lisa. Why doesn't he know this?*

"No, I want you to eat fifteen to eighteen hundred calories per day. This isn't a typical weight loss diet. You're training for a bodybuilding competition so you're going to need the calories to give you enough energy for all the exercising you're doing. Just trust me."

Whatever.

So I stick to the diet, mostly, but make a few substitutions here and there. Like milk, for example. The diet says I can't drink milk, juice, soda, coffee (?!) or anything else but water or green tea. But I view this meal plan as more of a guideline than something set in stone. Daniel seems to feel otherwise.

"Why are you drinking milk? It's not on the plan."

"I don't want to get osteoporosis."

"You get your dairy from the yogurt I gave you, plus you're taking a multivitamin and calcium pill. You don't need milk."

Daniel is a very black-or-white type guy. He and Regina would get along famously. I'm more shades-of-gray because that allows me to rationalize doing whatever it is I want to do. So since it seems he's actually going to *read* this food journal thing and bug me about it, I decide to outsmart him and not keep the journal at all.

"Lisa, why haven't you updated your food journal?"

"Oh, I've been busy with the kids. I'll do it tonight."

The next day I get a text.

Daniel: U forgot to update your food journal last night.

Really?!! You're going to text me about this? Didn't you read between the lines and know when I said, "I'll do it tonight" what I really meant was "I'll do it never"?

I CAN JUST EAT EVERYTHING AT THE END OF THE DAY, RIGHT?

My husband, Henri, is sitting on the couch watching TV and eating a bag of wavy potato chips with garlic cream cheese dip and a rum-and-Coke cocktail.

I sit next to him with a stack of food including: 4 oz. tilapia, 1 cup blueberries, cucumber slices, and some reheated quinoa.

"What the hell is that?" Henri asks, grimacing at the odd assortment.

"Well, I'm not used to eating six times a day, and there's so much food I can't eat it all, so I'm eating it now."

Before I started training I'd skip breakfast sometimes and then eat whatever around 10 a.m. along with a pot of coffee. Motherhood is tiring. I'd eat a Lean Cuisine for dinner and then chips, dip and cocktails after the kids went to bed. Now I'm eating tilapia and green beans. Every. Single. Day. *Blah!*

"I think you're doing it wrong," he says, biting an extra crunchy wavy potato chip with extra creamy cream cheese dip that makes me annoyed just looking at it, not because potato chips are annoying, but because it's annoying Henri can eat whatever he wants without gaining weight, because life is unfair.

"It's on the meal plan and I'm eating it or Daniel will call me out again for not following the stupid meal plan."

"Whatever." Henri drinks his cocktail. I look at my fish, blueberries, cucumbers, and quinoa and want to cry. But mostly I just want to eat chips.

The next day it's 6 a.m. and Daniel is at the trainer desk. He's looking at my online food journal. I hate that thing. I punch in my code. But I'm a little happy too because I'm in size 12 jeans now.

"So . . . what did you eat last night?" He looks perplexed.

"I didn't get a chance to finish everything on the meal plan, so I had to eat it at the end of the day," I explained, very proud of my culinary accomplishment.

"That's . . . no. No. You need to eat the food in the order I gave it to you. If you miss a meal, you miss it. Don't try to make up for it at the end of the day. I told you about macronutrients, right?"

"Uh huh."

Oh no. He's talking food vocabulary again. My mind wanders as he talks about protein, carbohydrates and fat percentages. I just thought I had to eat everything on the list. I didn't know there would be a time constraint on it. Dammit. I hate it when my husband's right! Why does this food thing have to be so complicated? Did I bring my workout gloves today? Oh no, I hope I didn't leave them at—

"Right?" He looks at me awaiting a response. I blink.

"Uh huh." *I don't even know what I just agreed to.*

"You didn't follow any of that, did you?" he smirks.

"Not a single word."

"Just follow the meal plan. If you miss something, you miss it, and move on. Let's go to the leg press."

When does the food thing get easier???

NAME THAT BLOG

It's been a very productive day. We held "The Diaper Ceremony" after my workout. The Diaper Ceremony involves having your toddler gather up all the diapers in the house, put them in a trash bag, and then throw them away in the *outside* trash can so he can make that connection: *This is the real deal. I* **have** *to use the potty now.*

But when Little Henry wasn't looking, Big Henri took all the diapers out of the trash and put them in the garage for later use. Big Henri's not about to waste $40 on symbolism. Little Henry is wearing his Go, Diego, Go! underwear and sweatpants (as they are easier for a toddler to navigate on and off than jeans) and I have the downstairs bathroom set up with a blue potty chair, and a basket full of exciting books, and we had a very constructive discussion about the merits of using a toilet versus a diaper.

Then he peed on the floor.

But this is just part of the process. I have him take off the wet clothes and put them in the washing machine, and have him help me clean up. See how I'm making him connect the consequences with his actions? It worked wonders with Rylee. She was potty trained in 10 days when she was 18 months old. It is my understanding that boys take longer than girls, so I have allotted two weeks for this process.

On the way out the door, Henri asked me to scan and email a lease for our new tenant. Scanning leases is a big fat pain in the ass. First, you have to convert it from legal to letter size, and then you have to do this one page at a time for each page because our scanner is so old it won't handle multiple sheets. But I'm trying to pay attention to Little Man so I can catch him before he goes. The potty training book that told me about the Diaper Ceremony said I'm supposed to take him to the bathroom every 30 minutes, but it neglected to mention whether the 30 minutes started from the top of the hour or from the point where he gets up off the potty. Because sometimes he's on there for like 20 minutes, and other times I have to practically hold him on the pot in a wrestler pose.

My cell phone rings.

"I need the lease, Lisa!"

"You know today was the Diaper Ceremony! I have to focus on Little Man."

"The tenant needs his lease. It's a little bit more important than getting a toddler to pee in a bowl."

"Why is everything you do more important than what I do?"

"I didn't say that. Why are you putting words in my mouth?"

I look over and Little Man is naked from the waist down running up the stairs. "Great! You made me miss it!" I hang up and clean the disaster on the floor.

I really could use a drink here. At least when I potty trained Rylee I could have wine.

But after a day of back-and-forth, I finally got Little Henry to use the potty once and was able to email Big Henri his lease. In between that I picked up Rylee, did the laundry, and started sorting all the receipts into piles so I could work on our taxes. Also, I sorted all the romance novels the library gave me into different genres: corset-rippers, cowboy, Danielle Steele books, Amish girl wanting an outsider, Highlander meets spunky lass, modern day trashy ones, and Nicholas Sparks tearjerkers.

By the time Big Henri comes home it looked like a giant had sneezed underwear and paperwork all over the house. I'm typing on the computer when he walks in the door.

"Hey." He looks at the piles of chaos everywhere.

"Hey. So what should I name my blog?"

"You're starting a blog now?" He drops his jacket on the floor, because God forbid he hang something up in the closet.

"I told you everyone said I needed to start a blog if I wanted to publish romance novels." *Duh.*

"And you need to do this now, because why?" He pulls out Home Depot receipts from his jeans pockets and throws them into my overflowing in-box.

"Daddy!" Rylee screams in glee and tackles him. Little Man wanders in half naked and sits on my lap.

"Because if I don't do it now, I think I'll never do it. I'm going to blog about trying to lose weight by entering a bikini competition. If I don't like blogging, then I can say it was only for the length of the training and stop at that point, and at least I'll have an online presence. But I don't know what to name it. I was thinking "The Bikini Project," but then people might think it was just a bunch of pictures of hot chicks in bikinis, and that's not really my audience. I want to appeal to women my age, you know?"

Little Henry is tapping on my keyboard and I manage to move my green tea just in time before he knocks it over.

"You're going to potty train our son, do the accounting for our business, write a romance novel, lose weight by training for a bikini competition, and, since that's apparently not enough, you're going to start a blog, too? She's Losing It.com"

He walks towards the kitchen.

"That's brilliant!" I say standing up with the baby. Yay! A blog is born!

STRUGGLING WITH THE WEIGHT

"Legs and glutes are one of the most important muscle groups for bodybuilding, especially for women," says Daniel.

I'm at the squat rack. Last week he just had me do squats with no weight until my form was right, and then he put just the bar with no weights on my back. Even that was heavy. Today he added weights to the bar, only I can't get it started because it's about two inches higher than I can reach. He laughs.

"Shorty." He pulls the bar down like it's nothing and readjusts all the settings and I'm a little thrown off by the comment because in my role as mommy, I'm usually the tallest person in the room.

"Let's try this again."

I achieve lift-off status and go down, but not far enough, apparently.

"Lower. Good. Keep your toes pointed forward. Good. That's one. Knees behind the ankle. Push through your heels. Head up. Breathe."

"That's a lot to think about without the benefit of coffee."

"Four. How's the diet going?"

"Good," I sputter.

"You're looking better. Six, seven, come on, push through your heels."

"I fit into my size ten jeans this morning!"

"That's awesome! Rest."

"I can't wait to fit into my size five jeans. When I was on *Buffy the Vampire Slayer* I actually fit into size three jeans. I weighed one hundred seven pounds. Do you think I'll be that skinny again?"

"We're going to keep you at this weight for now. Go again."

"Huh?" Then I realized he was talking about weight on the squat bar, not *my* weight.

"I think you need to stop worrying about weight on a scale. Three, four ... when you get to a certain point you don't even weigh yourself. Lower. That one didn't even count. Lower. Good. Seven, eight. Rest."

I'm struggling with the weight on my back, but also with the concept of not stepping on a scale. Is he nuts? How else do you know if you're on track? Every fitness magazine I've ever read said to weigh yourself so you hold yourself accountable.

We move to this push leg thingy. I sit on the chair that is at the bottom of the machine, position my legs kind of diagonally over my head and then release the weight safeties. The machine presses down until my legs are practically against my chest in the fetal position and then I push off with my feet until my legs are straight above me again. He starts with 90 lb., then increases it to 110 lb., and then finally 120 lb.!

"Holy crap! Did I just lift one hundred twenty pounds?!"

"You have really strong legs. It must be from all the running you used to do. But you never lifted weights before did you?"

"I worked with trainers before. I've done lat pulldowns and maybe eight-pound dumbbells but never really the machines. It was mostly just toning."

He rubs his hand over his lips and chin and looks over my body. "You're a little lopsided, strength-wise. We'll have to work on that."

He didn't explain beyond that, and we moved to leg extensions. "So, *Buffy the Vampire Slayer*, huh?"

"Yep. I had five lines during season four in an episode titled 'Beer Bad.' The reason I remember the title is because I still get three-dollar and ninety-four-cent royalty checks every quarter. I played a sorority girl named Paula who gets asked out by Xander, but she turns him down to date a guy who turns into a caveman. Life imitates art sometimes."

"You weighed one hundred seven pounds?"

"Yes," I beamed. That was the thinnest I've ever been, and I'm holding onto that memory for dear life. I refer to it as "My Buffy Weight: 107." I'm not alone in this. If you ask most women about the time when they were most in shape they will give the name followed by the precise poundage, saying something like, "My Wedding Weight: 134" or "My Cheerleader Weight: 115." That weight then becomes the bar against which all other weights are held against as baseline comparison. No diet has ever surpassed My Buffy Weight, which lasted barely three months, but those were the most exciting three months of my life.

"Bodybuilding is not about how skinny you are, it's about how good your muscles look, and that comes from strength training. You're not going to starve yourself. You *can't* starve yourself if you hope to follow the exercise schedule. Make sense?"

"Uh huh."

No. I don't care about strength training. I want My Buffy Weight.

BLOGGER CHALLENGE: LET THE POSTS BEGIN!

I know nothing about blogging. I used to keep a journal every single day, but too many people kept finding it and reading it and that really pissed me off. They were my thoughts! No one has a right to read my private thoughts but me! I wrapped up my journals and hid them in various safe places where no one could find them.

And now that I've been blogging for a week, I feel like I'm at the other extreme, where sometimes I just feel like I'm on the table at the gynecologist's office. Hi, World Wide Web! Yes, this is all of me, feel free to scrutinize. Please "Like" my Facebook page!

Actually, though, I love it. I love writing and reading other people's blogs. The fitness bloggers are a very supportive community. Everyone is either trying to lose weight or eat healthier while raising kids, training for some sporting event, and paying the bills. They are my virtual friends.

I'm taking part in a Blogger Challenge hosted by a blogger called Fitness Cheerleader. She writes out the topics for the month, and we have to write our post, link it to her site, and then comment on other people's stories. I'm glad she came up with this, because the only ideas I came up with were writing about the weather and a segment called "Dumb Shit I Said to my Trainer" (DSST). (Like, "DSST: Would your girlfriend train me for free?") We'll see how it goes!

(UN)FIT MAMA

I am committed to making this workout/family balance thing work. My biggest time management issue to date is fitting in cardio. The strength workouts take about 50 minutes, and if it were just that, I'd be fine. But since I have to lose weight, too, that means I have to do cardio 40 minutes a day. So an hour and a half of exercise plus shower and drive time turns into two hours in a blink. This requires me to test my schedule a little.

I thought afternoons would be best, after picking up Rylee from nursery school. There is a Kids' Club at the gym where you can drop off the kids for two hours while you work out. I feel guilty doing that though. See, I was a working mom for two years after Rylee was born and hated every moment of it. I felt so strongly about being a stay-at-home mom that I quit a six-figure senior management position and moved our family to a different state where we knew no one to accomplish that goal. Because I fought so hard for it, I feel guilty if I'm not with the kids 24/7. And what's really making me feel bad/confused/guilty is not so much that I'm dropping them off for an hour or two, but that I *look forward* to dropping them off for that long. So I devise a plan to avoid guilt and make everyone happy.

If I can wake up early enough, the ideal workout time is 5 a.m. because everyone is sleeping at home anyhow, and my husband doesn't have to adjust his schedule at all. But if I oversleep, or take 15 minutes too long in the shower, then it messes up the schedule to get Rylee to nursery school on time.

So lately it's just been easier for me to go to the gym twice a day, if you can imagine. I do the first part from 5 to 6 a.m. and then go back to the gym around 9 p.m. after the kids are asleep. This works because I don't cut into kid time and Henri always eats chips and drinks cocktails when he watches TV, so I just can't be around that right now—it's too tempting—so I have to avoid the situation entirely. So, in summary, the twice-a-day gym thing works *perfectly*.

Except when it doesn't.

I look at the time in the gym locker room and cringe. It's 7:15 a.m. I took too long in the shower, so now my husband is going to be a screaming basket case when I get home because he can't seem to get himself and the kids ready for school without my help.

It's 7:23 a.m. when I walk into the kitchen. Henri is arguing with Rylee over the speed of her cereal consumption (or lack thereof), the TV is blaring Umizoomi, and my son has ripped off his diaper (yes, we're back to diapers) and is doing a little naked dance before me. I know a puddle is awaiting my discovery somewhere. *Perhaps the timing of me learning weight training coinciding with my toddler's potty training is not a good mix.* My husband, Henri, shoots me a look.

"If you want me to have a bikini body, this is part of the deal, buddy," I say to him defensively. He doesn't answer me. He is pissed. Speaking of piss, I put a diaper on Little Henry, then Rylee and I head upstairs to get her dressed. It's PE day today at school, but she doesn't want to wear pants or sneakers and begins to cry.

"Pants are handsome; I want to look beautiful. I want to wear a dress." We compromise on a skirt with leggings and sneakers with fancy purple flowers. Then the battle over hair ensues. I pull out the comb from the drawer and she takes off running like a Kenyan sprinter at the Olympics. Maybe I should have put on her sneakers *after* combing her hair. . .

The gym was so lovely this morning. I drove there in the dark silence of the morning. Today I did my back workout on my own, following what I wrote down in my little notebook.

I get a text from Daniel. That kid lives on his phone.

Daniel: We need to work on ur form! No! You're pullovers weren't pullovers.

Daniel was in the gym this morning? I was doing it wrong?

Lisa: Sorry.

My husband is yelling something about his keys. All keys are supposed to go into the bowl on the kitchen counter immediately upon entering our house. When he follows this system our world is a happy world, but today he is running around berserk because he didn't follow the system and now has no idea where they are. He's also yelling about some lease he wants me to find RIGHT NOW.

Daniel: It's OK. Just don't want you to hurt yourself.
Lisa: Oh. OK.

"Who are you texting? LISA, WE NEED TO GET OUT NOW!"

All this drama because I showered a few extra minutes longer! Oh sure, I could take responsibility for driving my husband crazy with my consistent character flaw of running late, but I don't want to because he's YELLING AT ME! I'm not even sorry! So there!

"Rylee, either I fix your hair or you get a time-out. One, two—"

"Two and a half!" she says, exiting the castle tent and standing before me. I fix her hair, grab her lunch, and deposit her into my husband's truck.

Henri did not find his keys, but he did find the puddle my son made, and that's not helping his mood any. I find his keys for him, but now he's missing his cell phone. I hand him the lease he wanted and can't wait for the door to close.

"This is chaos, Lisa. Shower at home, or cut your gym time, or something. I can't do this every day." The door slams.

Will every morning be like this while I'm training? Do I just need to get up earlier? I'm already up at 5 a.m. I'm trying to make my exercise schedule have only a minimal impact on my family time. How do other women do this?

No Books for You!

Writers read. Did you know that Nicholas Sparks reads over 100 books a year? Of course, he makes millions of dollars writing his books and movies, so probably nobody bugs him when he's reading. The only thing I can really read during the day is books to Little Man while he sits on the potty seat.

By the way, potty training has been a Class A disaster. He knows how to do it, but he has no interest whatsoever in it. He likes being the baby and is miffed I'm attempting to change the status quo. Plus, when I was at the gym the other night, Big Henri put a diaper on Little Henry and now we're back to square one.

Anyway, it's tough reading at home because even if I lock myself in the bathroom, the kids will find me and bang on the door like crazy people wanting to get in. I'm never quite so interesting to them as when I need to use the bathroom. Also, Big Henri gets annoyed when I'm reading because that means I'm not paying attention to him. He can watch as much TV as he wants, but whenever I want to read, he will find new and creative ways to interrupt me.

But, being the resourceful person that I am, I've decided to multitask. I am now standing on the StairMaster with book in hand, ready to get lost in the story while burning 500 calories. Yes! Peace! Quiet! No interruptions!

"Lisa."

Daniel is standing next to me on the other StairMaster. *When the hell did he get there?* I trip a little.

"Oh, hi."

"Is that a good book?"

"Oh, yeah, it's a romance novel I'm reading. Nicholas Sparks . . . *The Notebook?*" Only, I'm reading his expression now, and it's saying to put the book away . . .

"You really shouldn't be reading on the machine; it slows you down."

"I know," I say feeling like a chastened child.

"How long have you been on the machine?"

"Uh, I don't know. Oh, it says thirty-two minutes."

"You don't look very sweaty."

"I know!" I smile. I consider this a good thing. I hate sweating, it's disgusting.

He is not impressed with my answer.

"Get an old sweater or a sweatshirt and wear it during cardio to get that water weight off you."

"OK." *Yuck.*

"Night." He smiles casually and walks away.

"Night."

"And get your hands off the rails," he calls out, not looking back at me.

I slide my hands off the rails . . . It's way harder walking on this thing when you're not holding the rails. Already I feel perspiration beading up on my forehead.

A pretty brunette is waiting for him near the front desk and they are flirting.

I wonder how long it's going to take him to go home so I can hold one rail and read my book again?

BLOGGER CHALLENGE: WHAT ARE YOUR THOUGHTS ABOUT THE MEDIA AND BODY IMAGE?

My perspective on this writing challenge is a little different from the other bloggers; I used to be an actress. By the time I was 23, I did back-to-back national tours playing Scout and Anne Frank in adaptations of *To Kill A Mockingbird* and *The Diary of Anne Frank*. I lived in New York City and did classical theatre Off Broadway. But I really wanted to get into television and film. Who doesn't want to be a movie star, right?

Well, here's the thing: A photograph adds 10 pounds to your look; video adds 20 pounds. So if you want to make it in LaLa Land, you need to be extra crispy thin. My problem was that I liked extra crispy fried chicken. Not a good mix.

Don't get me wrong, I was size 6 in New York, but before I moved to L.A. I went on a fitness kick *hardcore*. I was 25. I had never eaten well and could not afford a gym membership, but I really wanted to make it, so my roommate Erin helped me devise a meal plan of sorts.

She told me to eat six times a day and do cardio. She said I could have fruit in the morning and vegetables in the afternoon and I would need to switch from regular Pepsi to Diet Pepsi. My mom let me take her unused stepper machine to my Queens apartment (that was a fun subway ride) and I also bought kickboxing and yoga videos.

This was my routine every single day for six months:

<u>7 a.m</u>: Maple & brown sugar instant oatmeal, coffee with non-dairy creamer and Equal
<u>9 a.m</u>: Raisins
<u>11 a.m</u>: Salad (lettuce, cucumbers, carrots), chicken, Diet Pepsi
<u>1 p.m</u>: Celery sticks, carrot sticks
<u>4 p.m</u>: Baked potato with I Can't Believe It's Not Butter!® Spray
<u>6 p.m</u>: Pasta with cheese (!) and a glass of milk
Exercise 1 hour on stepper, then do 1 hour exercise videos.
<u>9 p.m</u>: Air popped popcorn with butter spray and salt

I got down to 107 pounds, the thinnest of my lifeLooking back at my diet, I see so many flaws! It seriously lacked protein. Not sure why cheese every night seemed like a good idea to me, but at 25 my metabolism was able to handle it.

My muscles were toned and I had some success. I was on an episode of *Buffy the Vampire Slayer* and also did a Ford commercial. But my career fizzed out and so did my diet and exercise regiment, for various reasons.

When I wasn't following my meal plan I would try any yo-yo diet out there, including diet pills and water pills, especially if I had an audition.

Being an actress is tough on the ego. You walk into a room filled with other people who look exactly like you—only better. Taller, thinner, better curves, bigger smiles. Talent only takes you so far.

The best body image compliment you could ever receive from someone was, "You look like you're ninety-nine pounds soaking wet." Whenever I heard that, my heart would soar because it meant I was thin enough to book a job.

Some people would say, "That's not fair; they should book based on talent." But that's the industry. The industry is based on looks and if you want to be in the game you have to play by their rules.

Well, at least those were the rules in 1999. Today I see a broader range of body types on TV. I think reality TV has opened doors to allow all types of body compositions into the mix, which is helpful for both viewers and actors.

My trainer is trying to help me get over the "99 pounds soaking wet" ideal, but it's hard to get rid of ideas ingrained in your psyche for so long. But I'll get there.

VALENTINE'S DAY

My first memory of Valentine's Day was when I was five. My father came home from working in New York City with two heart boxes of candy—a giant red one for my mother and a little pink box for me. It made me feel special and loved, and chocolate is always tasty.

Now that I'm an adult and training for a bodybuilding competition, chocolate is, of course, not on my meal plan.

Henri is excited that I'm losing weight and can fit into some of my old clothes. We couldn't get a babysitter, but he said he would cook me a meal at home. He went to the store and bought lobster tails and scallops and a nice bottle of wine. Also not on my meal plan, but how can you celebrate Valentine's Day with ground turkey and quinoa?

"The whole reason why you diet is so you can splurge occasionally, right?" he says, pouring the melted butter into a bowl.

"Uh huh." How much grief is my trainer going to give me for this meal?

But my husband is a fantastic cook. The lobster is divine and I forgot how amazing butter tasted. Wine too. There were also flowers . . . and a small box of chocolate.

Let me give you a little back story here. My husband never buys me chocolate on Valentine's Day because he always thought I ate too much of it and would gain weight. Instead he would get me the most gorgeous flowers on the earth—Brazilian roses, two dozen of them—and have them delivered to my office. I was the envy of every woman, and all the men in my office would say, "Thanks for making us look bad, Henri," which delighted him. But I always just wanted a box of chocolate, like what my father gave me.

I used to get him chocolate hearts, but being a dude, he's not that into chocolate, so he'd leave it on top of his dresser for months, until I couldn't take it anymore and I'd just eat it around July.

Finally, I had to explain to him that for me, a box of chocolate meant love, and even if he didn't understand, he should get it for me anyway because, if nothing else, it was what *I* wanted. So he would begrudgingly get me the little box of four truffles with the flowers, but it became a sore spot, so we just didn't go there anymore.

But now—now that I'm losing weight the right way through a healthy diet and exercise—now he buys me a box of chocolates?

"You've been doing so well, Lisa, I thought I'd spoil you a little," he said all sunshine and lollipops.

"I can't eat that," I say shifting in my chair. I'm thinking about what he just said. Everything about that sentence annoyed me, and now I'm pissed. "And you know that. Are you trying to sabotage me?"

"What!?! No, it's Valentine's Day. You're the one who likes chocolate. I was being nice," he said defensively.

"No, you were testing me." I get up from the table and grab the chocolates.

"Lisa, come on."

I walk out to the garage and put the box on a shelf. He is behind me.

"I can't have this shit around me. And you know that." I am glaring at him in the fluorescent lights.

"You're serious this time, aren't you?" His brows are furrowed and he has a trace of a smile on his face.

"Yes, so stop messing with me. Take that to work or something."

"OK, I'm sorry." He hugs me. "You're right, I didn't even realize it, but I was totally sabotaging you. I'm sorry."

WHO MOVED MY CHEESE?

There was a business book that was in vogue at the turn of the millennium called *Who Moved My Cheese?* by Spencer Johnson, M.D. and Kenneth Blanchard. The premise is that there are four mice and every day they run through their maze and eat their cheese, but one day at the end of the maze their cheese is gone and they have to deal with this situation. Two of the mice just put on their running shoes and search for the cheese without much drama, and the other two mice (I believe their names were Hem and Haw) are just having serious issues dealing with their cheese being moved. It's an analogy for dealing with change.

It was a quick read and a funny book and I found it somewhat silly. Until someone moved *my* cheese, or in this case, a belief that had thus far been unchallenged in my mind. I discovered I'm not very good dealing with change or accepting new ideas.

New Idea: When training for a bodybuilding competition, it is important to consume more (not fewer) calories.

This goes against every single dieting principle I've been taught since watching my mother diet in the ' 70s. Everyone knows that weight loss is just simple math (which explains why I hate it so much): Fewer calories consumed + more calories burned = skinny Lisa.

So when Daniel tells me he wants me to eat between 1,500 and 1,800 calories per day, I think he's on crack. Now, I ask you, would you take advice from a crack addict? Me neither. So I skipped a meal or two. But damn it, he's still reading that stupid food journal and calling me out on it.

"You're not eating enough calories, Lisa," he reprimands while clicking through my journal.

"But I want to lose weight." Stupid food journal.

"Stop focusing on the scale and just look at your body. Numbers on a scale mean nothing. You have to trust me on this one."

BUT YOU'RE MOVING MY CHEESE!!! HOW CAN I LOSE WEIGHT IF I'M EATING MORE? YOU'RE SO TOTALLY, ENTIRELY WRONG!!! AND . . .

I tried on my size 8 jeans and they fit.

Back to the *Who Moved My Cheese?* book—the two mice resisting change had to eventually make a decision: face their fears of the new and unknown with the promise of eventually finding cheese somewhere, or resist change and starve to death. I guess I'll be the brave mouse and bounce my head against the walls of the maze for a time. Who knows? Maybe the new cheese I find will be even better than what I knew before.

GYM RATS

Now that I am going to the gym twice a day, I've been noticing that there are other crazy people like me who live at the gym too. We'll call them the gym rats.

Some people work out and get in a "zone." Daniel says he is a "zone person" and just is completely focused on his regimen. I am a "people watcher," which is to say I probably should be more focused on what I'm doing but it's way more interesting to watch other people.

The Ladies

- **Pink Hair Lady** is a 5 a.m. person. Her hair is in a short bob and is entirely pink. She looks about my age, maybe a little older, and also looks like she could totally kick the sh** out of someone if they messed with her. She does high intensity mountain climbers on the treadmill (?!!) and I can't help but stare. Plus, I mean, come on, she has pink hair. You don't dye your hair pink if you want to go unnoticed.

- **Thin Tan Lady** is ripped. She must be a size 0 and a size 2 if she is soaking wet. She has brown hair that is always in a ponytail and her muscles are finely chiseled. I notice that she does not lift super heavy weights and her form is always perfect. I've seen her there at all hours—5 a.m., 9 p.m., and sometimes in between. I wonder if she has kids? She looks younger than me.

- **Blonde Trainer Chick** is intimidating to me. I saw her jump from the floor to the top of a three-foot-high step stool without blinking. She did this like 20 times in a row. She is like a cheetah. Who does that? She is usually with clients. The only time I saw her work out was one Saturday doing those jumps.

The Gents

- **Tattoo Arm Man**. I will confess: he is my eye candy. I was on the stepper machine and he was on this back extension equipment in front of me where his arms were behind his neck and he bent over and then lifted up. He has *nice* biceps. Again, you don't tattoo your arms and work them out if you don't want people to look at them, right?

- **2012 College Kid** has made great strides in his bodybuilding. He is at the gym morning and night and seems to be in the zone all the time. I don't think I've ever even seen him turn his head. It's always facing front and his expression is blank. But the weights he holds keep getting bigger and I see a lot more definition in his arms.

- **Crew Cut Treadmill Guy** reminds me of Jim Carville, the Democrat who ran Bill Clinton's campaign who's on all the Sunday morning political talk shows, only with hair. Crew Cut Treadmill Guy is a morning workout person and I only recently saw him branch out into weights. He mostly likes the treadmill only.

I also like watching the **Mother/Daughter Team**. The mother has short dark hair and the daughter has brown hair in a ponytail. They do cardio side by side and weights together too. I think it would be cool to team exercise with my daughter someday.

Sometimes people stop going to the gym, or maybe they just work out at different times from me now. I have seen neither Pink Hair Lady nor Tattoo Arm Man in awhile. I'm curious where they went. I wonder if they will ever come back? I wonder if they know I watch them sometimes and if they are OK with that?

I wonder if people are starting to watch me now? Because I am slowly transforming into a gym rat too.

R U Going 2 Txt Me?

"How's it going?" Daniel appears from nowhere, startling me so much I almost fall off the damned StairMaster again. He is omnipresent it seems.

"I feel good," I reply as I shrug a smile and pull off my iPod earphones. *(See? I'm not reading. I get bonus points for that, right?)* "Guess what? I fit into my size six jeans!! I just skipped size seven entirely and went from size eight to size six, which makes no sense, but then again, my body never makes sense!"

"That's great!" He gives me a high five, then, "Aren't you supposed to do the treadmill today?"

I hate the treadmill. It's boring. They only show ESPN on that side of the gym.

"Was that today?" I play dumb. I'm blond after all. But he's not . . .

"You need to follow the work-out calendar I gave you."

"OK," I say, descending from the machine. I wipe my face with the white towel they gave me at reception. It feels rough against my skin.

"I feel like you're not communicating with me enough."

"Huh?"

"If you see me in the gym, you can say 'Hi' or ask a question, you know."

"Well, I don't want to bug you . . ."

This is partly true. When I worked, I used to go to the fitness center in my building and use the elliptical machine. I stopped going because all my clients used to interrupt my exercising to give me laundry lists of things they wanted me to do for them. I never want to be *that* client to him, or interrupt him if he is training other people. That's fair to neither him nor his clients.

The other part of the truth is that I avoid Daniel like the plague. I feel like I'm doing everything amiss and he always seems to notice and will send me texts like, "We need to work on your form on some of your back exercises! R u getting good activation?" or "No! Your pullovers weren't pullovers," or "Stop holding the rails on the treadmill!!!"

Half the time I didn't even know he was in the gym, let alone noticing all the stuff I was doing wrong. Then I realized that Stealth Ninja Trainer lives in the gym. He sleeps on the treadmill and his pillow is a 50 lb. weight.

"I keep pretty good tabs on all my clients, and I feel like you're not communicating enough. You're paying a lot for training sessions. If you have a question about the exercises, or form, or your diet, you should text me."

"Um, OK . . ."

I will never text him.

DON'T GO TOO HEAVY! PLUS GUACAMOLE RECIPE

Later that same day . . .

The kids are in bed and I'm showing off to my husband as a commercial for Pizza Hut blares in the background.

"Henri, I'm getting so strong! I lifted forty pounds on the cable curl the other day. Feel my muscle." I raise my arm and squeeze a tight fist. A teeny, tiny muscle waves back.

"Don't use too much weight, Lisa," he says, placing the guacamole on the coffee table.

I roll my eyes at him. Sometimes Henri is just a know-it-all because he lifted weights when he was younger. "I'm not using too much weight. Plus, Daniel says the middle weight I lifted in my last set should be the start weight the next time I work that muscle group."

"You don't need to use heavier weights. If you use lighter weights and go slower, that's just as effective."

"Oh, Henri, come on. I think it's cool that I'm getting baby muscles in my arms."

"Yes, Lisa, it's cool you're getting buff again."

We settle down on the couch and start watching *Up All Night* with Christina Applegate. I am munching on cucumber slices and homemade guacamole that Henri made for me. It was a tip my first trainer, Chris, gave me last Thanksgiving (when I started going back to the gym). Guacamole and cucumbers sounds like an odd food combo, but it tastes good together. It helps me to get the last two cups of vegetables into my diet because it feels more like junk food than vegetables.

Here's a secret: Henri is WAY better at cooking than I am. His guacamole is truly scrumptious. Here's the recipe:

Enrique's Guacamole (FYI—*Enrique* is Spanish for Henry and I wanted the recipe to sound fancy.)

¼ avocado
¼ cup tomatoes
¼ cup onions
¼ cup salsa
4 strands cilantro
1 teaspoon jalapeño
And don't forget a splash of lime juice!

Dice everything, put in a bowl and mix.

Serve with 1 cup of cucumber slices instead of chips.

Total calories: 149.

INJURY!

The next day . . .

Today is chest/shoulder day. This is not a training day; I do everything on my own. I am speeding through all the exercises and feel pretty proud of myself. I keep adding heavier and heavier weights because I feel really strong today.

Remember I told you about the guy in the sauna who was talking about the pigs right before I started training with Daniel? OK, well, his name is James, and he is at the gym most mornings. He owns a farm and has two daughters and he comes over and sits down to do seated lat pulldowns. I am standing diagonally from him doing cable curls. I start at 40 lb. *Piece of cake!*

He compliments me—says it looks like I'm losing weight.

He's right. My size 6 jeans are loose! Loose, I tell ya! And, cross your fingers, at this rate I might be able to squeeze into my size 5 jeans by the end of the week! Oh sure, they probably won't zip, but f*** it—I will safety pin the top and throw an oversized T-shirt on top just to say I'm in size 5 jeans.

James talks about his youngest daughter, the 3rd grader, who was at the horse show yesterday. She was nervous because there were some girls in the competition who had sponsors and professional trainers and she didn't.

I increase the weight to 50 lb. *Whoa. This is getting heavy.* Sweat beads on my brow.

His other daughter is unfazed and just rides the horse . . .

I increase the weight to 60 lb. *Oh my God, this is heavy.* I'm trying to face him as he speaks because it seems rude not to, and then I feel a SHARP pain in my left shoulder. I wince, drop the weight, and roll my shoulder back and forth, pinching it with my right hand.

The weight was too heavy. Damn! Henri was right (again).

I say goodbye to my friend and move to the free weights.

This is just a temporary pain, I think to myself as I do arm raises with 8 lb. weights. But the pain is getting worse and I just can't concentrate. I pinch the muscle again in hope that it is just a knot but now I'm seeing spots and I head to the locker room.

The older woman who swims all the time is there. "Honey, you don't look good," she says worried.

"I can't move my arm." I am almost crying from the pain and I consider calling my husband to come pick me up, but I have the car with the car seats, so there's no way he can drive the truck with the kids. I'll just have to drive home with one arm.

I send Daniel a one-handed text from the parking lot.

Lisa: So, just thought I would communicate with you. . . . I injured myself doing cable curls. I'm driving to the doctor now.

WILL YOU MARRY ME AGAIN?

Every morning I get out of bed, take off my clothes, and weigh myself. (I'm a firm believer that pajamas easily add 17 pounds to the scale.) On New Year's I was 150 pounds. The first day I started training with Daniel I was 146 pounds. Now, not even a month later, I'm 134 pounds and I just can't believe it.

The scale used to be hidden and reviled and now it has become a curiosity for me. Each morning I'm excited to see the numbers go down. I fit into clothes I haven't seen in years and other areas of my life are changing in novel ways.

My shoulder is still inflamed from pulling it yesterday, but that doesn't stop me from trying on a stack of shirts that suddenly fit me. Shopping in my closet leads me to memories long past. Today I discovered my white Bebe skirt and black lace tank top. I bought them for our trip to Rome seven years and two kids ago and blushed at the memory of the trip.

"There's your fountain," I waved offhandedly, the sting of the past still fresh in my mind.

"Come on, we have to get closer," he says with surprising urgency.

He takes my hand and pulls me through the crowd. The heat and humidity of the July afternoon feel like a heavy blanket suffocating me. A vendor weaves through with red roses for sale and I feel the ghost of hurt again. I don't want to be here.

"You have to take a coin and throw it into the fountain so we can come back."

"We've done this before, Henri."

"Lisa, please."

Some German university students are singing loudly in drunken euphoria, wrapped in their country's flag like a Super Man cape. Their team made the World Cup playoffs. Tourists snap pictures around us.

"Sit down. Now close your eyes and throw the coin," he said as though this were the first time we were here. I exhaled in annoyance.

"Fine."

The fountain's edge was cool from the shade of the buildings. Water from the majestic sculptures splashed on the back of my neck and it felt cool on my skin. Closing my eyes, I tossed the coin into the Fontana di Trevi—the Trevi Fountain. Opening my eyes, I discovered Henri down on his knee holding a wooden box, my wedding ring resting in the satin center, only with a much bigger diamond in it.

"Will you marry me again? This is the proposal you should have had the first time."

Will you marry me again?

Yes!

YOU AGAIN

When I was working (before having the kids) I could literally spend 40 minutes curling my hair if I had an important meeting to attend that day. My make up was applied neatly, my fingernails manicured.

I was a hard-working and dedicated Senior Manager and was rewarded financially for my efforts. When you have extra cash and no responsibilities beyond yourself, it's easy to look good.

Enter children.

Spit up on your shoulder does not really finish out the polished look most people are going for. My daughter was fond of yanking my hair while my son preferred dislodging earrings from my lobes. I think my jewelry box has at least seven sets of earrings missing their match, but I keep the singles in hopes of one day finding the other buried somewhere behind a sofa cushion.

My nails are cut to the quick now (short nails work better with Play Doh). And polish? Oh please!

Eighteen months ago my hair looked like it was styled by a polygamist wife from an episode of *Big Love*, so I took drastic measures, and, well . . . my hair is slowly growing out from the really short bob that seemed like a good idea at the time.

But today . . . today I feel good. Today I look pretty.

By a freak of nature, both children are napping upstairs, my husband is talking on the phone in another room, and standing in my closet I have discovered that my size 5 jeans fit. They are dark blue and have brown and tan flowers embroidered above the top left pocket and on the front right leg starting below the knee and flaring out at the boot cut bottom.

For the past four years my wardrobe rotation included five black v-necks and a turquoise T-shirt that said "Jersey Girls Don't Pump Gas." Today I am wearing a brown tank top with spaghetti straps.

I straighten my hair and curl the ends under, letting them fall loosely on my collarbone. Opening my makeup bag I put on a little mascara and some lipstick, just because. I find some pink nail polish and shake it for a minute or two. It's been awhile since I painted them.

Henri finishes his conversation and walks into our bathroom where I am standing in front of the mirror. "Wow," he says simply.

I smile shyly. I look at his hazel eyes in the mirror. I look at him looking at me. He stands behind me now and he is smiling too. His lips lightly brush against my shoulder and he whispers softly in my ear, barely audible, those words I've been longing to hear for almost half a decade . . .

You're you again.

WEIGH-IN #2—WHAT ARE YOU REALLY HUNGRY FOR?

Daniel is at the training center computer and smiles as I walk up. "Does your shoulder feel better? Are you ok to lift?"

"The doctor said most of the injury was caused by sitting at the computer the wrong way. I guess blogging is high-risk too."

He laughs and we walk to the scale. Today is weigh-in. I always wear black sweatpants and a large T-shirt for the training sessions, but today I'm wearing my "Run Like A Girl" shirt I got when I finished the Nike Marathon in 2006. That was the last time I was in shape.

"Bet you haven't worn that shirt in a while." He gives me a high five.

I feel embarrassed and I'm not sure why, so I make a joke. "Diet and exercise work. Who knew?"

"Everyone," he says, laughing.

The weight is just melting off me. I can't believe how fast this is happening! It's . . . too fast. I wasn't expecting the results to come so quickly, and even though my body is much happier, my mind has been playing tricks on me.

I weigh 136 pounds. Even though this is 10 pounds lighter than my first weigh in, I secretly know that I was 134 pounds a few days ago, but I've been cheating on the diet. He takes my measurements and says I'm right on target. But then he notices my face.

"Everything all right?" He looks perplexed.

"Yep. Well. I don't know," I stammer. I feel like I'm going to cry but I don't. How do I tell him that even though I wanted to lose weight, now that I have, I feel uncomfortable? People are complimenting me, which is great, but I'm not used to so much attention. I've been kind of invisible for a few years and now I'm not.

And what if I'm suddenly not as likeable to my friends? When I got in shape to move to L.A. some of my friends started saying mean things behind my back, just loud enough for me to overhear. I know they were actor friends and jealous that I was booking roles, but it really hurt and I never really dealt with it.

Well, that's not true. I dealt with it by eating whenever I got really close to my goal weight. So I dealt with it; I just never resolved it.

"Lisa, you look amazing. Look how far you've come in only three weeks!" he says trying to cheer me up.

At home I can't really focus. I just feel ~~hungry~~ . . . I just have to eat something . . .My stomach is churning and I'm anxious. I try to follow the meal plan, but then I suggest to Rylee that she have a grilled cheese sandwich for lunch.

"Ok, Mommy." She's sitting at the table with Henry, playing with some cars. I butter the bread and put some cheese between and then pull out two more slices—for me. I'm thinking of those women in the locker room who gave me a dirty look yesterday. I'm thinking of one of the dads at Rylee's nursery school who said, "Wow! You look great. Did you get your hair cut or something?"

"Yeah, a ten-pound haircut," I chuckled. But I felt weird because he complimented me in front of his wife. Would she be mad at me? Why should she be? But what if she is?

I sprinkle salt on my grilled cheese sandwich, but one is not enough so I make another, all the while knowing that I should not be doing this.

I bite into the first grilled cheese, find comfort in the heat, enjoy the flavor of the butter and cheese and the texture of the bread on my tongue. I am simultaneously calmed and repulsed while chewing, inexplicably on the verge of tears and then consider that in addition to everything else, I am clearly neurotic too.

Rylee and Henry are done and are off devising some complicated game, while I play my own complicated internal food misery game. Staring at the second grilled cheese sandwich I feel full. I should not eat this. I take a bite.

Will Regina still like me?

Because we both started with trainers at the same time and my results are faster. I can't lose her as a friend. She is my only real friend here. I finish the food, tasting nothing, and then decide to send her an email, because I'm too scared to speak to her directly.

SELF-SABOTAGE—PART 1

Subject: Just saying hi and venting a little
From: Lisa
Date: Thu, 1 Mar 2012 1:39 PM
To: Regina

Hi Regina,

How are you? I miss our Thursday breakfasts now that your son is in nursery school and our boys don't take Spanish together anymore. Need to vent . . . about myself actually.

I've been working out like crazy, following the diet very strictly, and surprise of surprises, diet and exercise works for me. Henri is happy. People are saying I look better. But . . . I heard two women talking at the gym yesterday, complaining about how difficult it is to lose weight and they looked at me like I could never understand and I suddenly felt like an outsider. So what do I do? Go home and eat four York Peppermint Patties and drink an entire pot of coffee with flavored creamer. And a grilled cheese sandwich. And popcorn. With butter. I am the queen of self-sabotage.

My trainer asked me what was up today since I kept getting light-headed and I told him I didn't eat breakfast so I could cut down my calories. He lectured me about following the meal plan and being consistent. He said I lost 3% body fat in three weeks and should be proud of myself. I told him it feels like I'm never going to get my body back, I'm never going to have a flat stomach again. He said I'm too hard on myself; I've held the extra weight for almost five years now and had two C-sections so it was insane for me to think that it would turn into a six-pack in one month.

He's right, of course, but who ever said I was logical? He told me to just trust him and follow the meal plan and eat more calories. (I've been cutting the calories down to 1,400 a day instead of the 1,800 in the plan.) So after the workout I took Henry to Spanish school and then went to Waterloo and ordered a ham and cheese omelet with hash browns (with salt) and buttered biscuits. I'm pretty sure that's not what he meant by eating more calories. What the hell is wrong with me?

OK. From this moment on I'm going back on the diet and I'm not going to even think about what other people think of me. It's OK to be healthy, and losing weight doesn't mean I lose friends, cause that's just silly. And I'm telling you this so I can hold myself accountable. All right. Thank you for letting me vent.

Hope you are doing well.

Lisa

REGINA ROCKS!

Subject: Re: Just saying hi and venting a little
From: Regina
Date: Thu, 1 Mar 2012 18:33:09 -0600
To: Lisa

I miss our Thursdays too. Vent away. Let me just say a BIG screw you to those bitches. This is a problem THEY are having. Maybe they were looking at you wishing they were already where you are. It doesn't matter what size you are compared to others; it matters where you are for YOU. Listen to your emotionally healthy friend, the work you are doing for YOU is just as hard as the work I am doing for me. Don't destroy yourself to fit in (either heavier or lighter). Stay on your path and you will get there. I'm here for you.

Regina

You know what? Regina is right! Why am I making myself less just to fit in? That's so stupid. So, yeah, screw you bitches! And screw you mean actor girls from NYC too! 'Cause I'm going to make myself a bikini body now.

ONE BEER'S OK, RIGHT?

Did you know that March 2nd was Texas Independence Day? I didn't either, until I read it on the drink list specials at the bar Henri and I went to with our friends Dave and Lucrecia. I was super excited to get out of the house for a double date and wear my new (old) clothes. I could fit into my jean skirt and could once again zip up my calf-high boots.

I was feeling pretty proud of myself. I only ordered one beer . . . at a bar . . . on Texas Independence Day! That is a total sign of self-control right there. I followed the meal plan religiously all morning and afternoon, so in my mind, dinner was not a big deal.

The hors d'oeuvres on the table were hummus, carrots, and pita triangles. Carrots are vegetables, right? I only ate half the steak slices and maybe four or five French fries that came later, so, again, I was practically breaking my arm patting myself on the back about maintaining moderation in a public setting.

Alas, my happy state of denial was met with a reality check: there is no such thing as moderation when you're training for a fitness competition, just rigid adherence to your diet.

Monday morning came and Daniel asked how my weekend went. And I was dumb enough to answer honestly.

"You ate WHAT?" The look I received from him was a cross between frustration, disappointment, and I dare say a touch of pissed-offedness.

"No, you don't understand. It was ONE beer. Just one. It was Texas Independence Day ... ," I explained, my voice steadily growing octaves higher with each lame justification.

"Do you even care about getting in shape?"

His question just kind of hung in the air as he stared at me. I felt about two inches tall.

"Well, yes," I muttered defensively.

"Because your competition is in three months and you can't be ready if you keep cheating on your diet. Alcohol is so bad for you, Lisa. Your body can't restore its muscles because it's too busy trying to clean out all the toxins you just put in it. I'd rather you told me you ate junk food than alcohol."

"Well, I did some of that too . . . ." I confessed sheepishly.

He shook his head and walked to the free weights. I followed, feeling really awful.

Damn, I've been served.

HELD ACCOUNTABLE

I came home from the gym to the aroma of cinnamon raisin bagels.

"How did your training session go?" asked Henri, smearing cream cheese on his totally wonderful smelling bagel that I can't eat.

"Awful, just awful. Daniel was upset that I drank a beer. ONE beer. Can you believe it?" I asked, complete with righteous indignation.

Henri laughed. "I like this guy. He's the only trainer who ever held you accountable," he said, pouring a third teaspoon of sugar into his coffee.

I can't have coffee. I can't have sugar.

"Oh, shut up, Henri," I muttered, leaving the kitchen to avoid the smell of food I couldn't eat. Henri followed me into our bedroom.

"Why am I even doing this stupid competition? I'm not going to win it. I could eat more things when I was pregnant. Stupid bikini competition," I muttered, pulling off my sweaty T-shirt and throwing it on the counter.

"Lisa, I'm so proud of you. In four weeks you dropped seven dress sizes. That's insane. You're wearing clothes you haven't fit into in years. Whatever he's having you do is working, right?"

"Right," I mumbled, turning on the shower. Henri tapped my shoulder and I faced him.

"OK, so you had a tough morning. He held you accountable. That's good; it means he really wants you to meet your own goals and isn't just in it to sell you more sessions. He's a good trainer."

So much for spousal sympathy. I guess I'll just have to stick to the damn diet.

EXHAUSTED

It's Wednesday morning, not even 8 a.m., and I'm exhausted. Last night I was at the gym till damn near midnight, and then I was up again this morning at 5 a.m. The receptionist at midnight was still on shift when I came back this morning and we exchanged one of those, "Weren't you just here, crazy lady?" looks and then laughed.

I do 45 minutes of cardio and then my planks, which take about 30 minutes. After that I change into my black tankini and head to the spa area holding a towel over my smaller yet still flabby stomach and wish I could fast forward to when I will be able to look good in a real bikini again.

Remember when I said if I were a size 8 I would dance naked in my living room? Yeah, that never happened. Because even though I am now officially size 5, I still don't feel confident enough to undress in the locker room. When will these weird rolls of skin around my waist go away? I change in the bathroom, behind closed doors. Now here comes the fun part.

To make things more interesting for myself, I set up a little game: I only go into the Jacuzzi if it's already turned on. Otherwise, I just head to the steam room for about 15 minutes. I'm a firm believer in rewarding myself, and pretending to be in a fancy spa is my reward for exercising so much I don't know whether it's day or night.

This next comment will only make sense to mothers of small children. When I'm done in the steam room, I get to do my favorite thing ever: shower *alone*! I pack my own shampoo and conditioner and get to dress in peace and quiet for a change.

After I get home and get Rylee off to nursery school, I take a breath. Now it's just me and little Henry. I sit him on the potty and read *Big, Bigger, Biggest!* by Nancy Coffelt. It's one of those picture books that helps build vocabulary.

Looking at the title I think, "This is how I felt in my bathing suit." We read on. Henry is enjoying the pictures. The hungry pig reminds me I haven't eaten my meal two yet.

I lean my head against the sink. The sleepy squirrel picture is pushing me over the edge.

Henry says, "All done Mama!" climbs off the potty, and then, like clockwork, pees on the floor.

I wish I could drink a Red Bull, but it's not on the diet. Neither is coffee. Grr. I try to convince Little Man to take a nap. *Come on kid! Be the drowsy squirrel!* He is more interested in tugging on my ears than sleeping.

It's time to pick up Rylee from nursery school. I put on the radio to wake myself up. We get home and Rylee wants to play but I want to crash. Little Henry grows heavy with sleep against my chest. I love the way babies feel when they fall asleep in your arms.

"Mommy, I have an idea! Let's play Scooby Doo and Rylee!"

Zoinks! I don't want to! "Let's play the nap game."

"No, that's no fun!"

I'm not above bribery.

"If you let Mommy sleep for thirty minutes, I will give you a GoGurt."

"Deal."

Zzzzzzzzzzz

WEIGH-IN #3—BABY FAT

I was only supposed to have the 10 training sessions as my combined Christmas/birthday gift since they are really expensive and money is tight right now, but Henri loves the results and so he agreed to let me purchase another 10 pack. We're doing a payment plan where it's divided into three payments on our credit card.

I meet Daniel at the check-in area. Today is weigh-in and measurements day, plus I'm buying the 10 pack. I'm distracted and stressed out. I've been keeping a secret from my husband and with each passing day I panic more.

"Everything OK?" Daniel's processing the training purchase in the computer.

"I think I'm pregnant," I blurt out.

"Whoa." He moves the keyboard my way and I absentmindedly type in my credit card info. "Do you and your husband use protection?"

"I'm on the pill. So I don't know how this can be happening." I'm pulling my hair behind my ear. *This can't be happening. We can barely afford the two we have.*

"Well, how late are you? Like two weeks . . . three days . . . ?"

"Yeah, three days." *Damn size 5 jeans with the flowers on the pocket . . .*

I step on the scale. He writes it down in my file. I mentally note that I weigh more than I did two days ago. *Probably because I'm pregnant again . . .*

"Well, you've been pregnant before. Does it feel the same? Are you more tired than usual?"

"Yes, but I'm also exercising twice a day. And my kids never sleep. I'm always tired." *And think how tired I'll be with a third. The kids will outnumber us . . .*

He takes out that dreaded pincher thing that measures body fat and starts pinching different parts of my body and writing the measurements down.

I'm just spilling out whatever pops into my brain now, more to me than him. "We have our own business. Our insurance doesn't cover maternity costs. Plus we still have a hospital bill for Little Henry."

"Look, I'm not a doctor or anything, but if you're on the pill you're probably not pregnant. Your body is probably just reacting to all the diet and exercise changes."

This gives me a glimmer of hope. "I did make a lot of changes," I consider.

He pulls out a container of whey protein. "Foot up." I place my foot on it and he has me pinch the top of my thigh so he can measure it.

"I hope no one drinks from that thing if my foot is on it."

"Huh? No, this has been under the table since I started working here. We just use it as a step stool for measurements." He writes the number down. "I mean, think about it, in one month you changed your entire food intake, dropped from size fourteen to size five, and started working out twice a day. *In one month.* Of course your body is going to get a little confused."

He pinches my calf to take the measurement. It hurts like hell and I wince.

"Yeah, you're right. I'm totally not pregnant."

"Right. . . . But take a pregnancy test, though."

OOPS BABY?

I drive home from the gym and my thoughts are all over the map. *I'm not pregnant. This is just a cruel joke my body is playing on me because I'm making it function properly again.* Andrew is a nice name if it's a boy. We could call him Drew or Andy. I hope it's not a girl; I hear sisters fight more than brothers. Although Lexi or McKenzie or Brooklyn would be cute names. How will Little Henry react to being the middle child?

How will Big Henri react to having a third child at 50? He's going to look at me and say, "Ah, hell no!" and he's going to blame this on me, as though I were the only participant in this situation.

I go inside and pretend that everything is fine. Henri takes Rylee to school and I decide to look for the extra pregnancy test that was a leftover from when I found out I was pregnant with Little Henry. It's in the upstairs bathroom. I will take the test . . .

. . . after I do a load of laundry.

Or maybe five loads of laundry. I keep trying to convince my family to join a nudist society in an effort to reduce my housework but no one seems interested. Except Little Henry. He will strip naked anywhere.

I bring the test into my bathroom. I wonder if the asparagus I ate will affect it? Or the supplements? Maybe protein powder increases HGH levels? *I'm not pregnant. This is just from the exercise.* And this test will put my mind at ease, so I'm going to take it . . .

. . . right after I vacuum.

Housework is tedious and soul crushing, so I like to wear my wedding tiara when I do it—that way I can pretend I am a princess. Four hours later the house is spotless, the wood cabinets are polished, and I finally take the stupid pregnancy test.

It says it will take 3–5 minutes . . .

. . . it's flashing now.

It will say NOT PREGNANT very clearly. . . .

. . . still flashing . . .

Unless it says PREGNANT . . . oh, come on stupid thing just tell me what I have to deal with!

ERROR???!!!!!?????? *How can I have an* ERROR *message?!?!? What does that even mean?!?*

It's 6 p.m. and my husband comes home from work. He's got a funny look on his face. "Hi, honey, the house looks beautiful . . . is everything OK?"

He knows something is up; the house is only this clean when I'm pregnant or my mom is coming to visit. "Remember how we discussed having a third child?"

He looks at me with a half smile and I feel calmed because he's smiling and not angry, which makes what I'm about to say even easier.

"Well, thank God it was just hypothetical because I'm not pregnant!"

He exhales, "Thank God," and laughs. "I saw the pregnancy test box in the trash and got nervous . . . but hey, at least the house is clean."

THAT '70s MOM

"You look overwhelmed," said Daniel.

"I'm just thinking about all the time I'm going to have to spend in the gym. I feel like I live here."

"You're not here *that* much."

"Well I'm here at five a.m. until seven a.m. and then I come after the kids are asleep, around nine thirty p.m. so I don't get home till eleven p.m. and—"

"And you can't fall asleep because your endorphins are on overdrive, right?"

"Right."

"You need more sleep."

"But I try to not have my workouts impact my kids."

"We have Kids' Club here. You could work out in the afternoons."

"But they don't like Kids' Club."

"Can't you just be a mom and say, 'You're going?'"

Now, the short answer to his question is, "Yes, of course," but the more accurate answer really is, "It depends." See, Daniel is a young guy and has a dog but not kids, and until you have kids you really can't understand that sometimes it's not about you, it's about what's right for your kids.

Parenting today seems a lot different than when I grew up in the late ' 70s. Take pregnancy, for example. When I was pregnant with Rylee and Henry, I had no coffee, no soda, no alcohol, and no sushi. I did not dye my hair and I exercised daily (by "exercised" I mean "walked around the block"). When my mom was pregnant with me, she smoked a pack a day and had the occasional cocktail to "take the edge off."

As a child I can remember rolling around in the back of the station wagon (there were no seatbelts, let alone car seats, thank you very much) and going to the bowling alley. My mom bowled in the league with the other moms and I played in the babysitting area for hours, it seemed. I don't remember being bothered by it, but then again, if I complained too loudly she would say, "Knock it off, or I'll smack you a shot." And by all measures, I had a very good childhood.

If someone caught me "smacking a shot" at my kids, they would probably record it on their smart phone and it would probably go viral and Congress would probably enact a law called the Anti-Smack-A-Shot-Law to prosecute abusive mothers. So I'm left to try to reason with my four-year-old at nursery school pick up, who is not necessarily the most reasonable child anyway.

"Guess where we're going today?"

"Where?"

"Kids' Club!!"

"No! I don't want to go there, Mommy! Can't we please go home?"

"Why don't you like Kids' Club?"

"Because they don't let the moms in and I want to play with you."

See Daniel? I'll bet your dog doesn't give you a guilt trip when you go to the gym.

"Well, honey, we'll play together after I work out."

"Can't you work out at night when I'm asleep?"

"Rylee, I'm getting too tired." She was not interested in my exhaustion, so I switched tactics. "Look, I do lots of nice things for you and your brother, like take you to nursery school in the mornings and take Henry to Spanish class. The gym is my fun thing to do."

"BUT I DON'T WANT TO GO TO KIDS' CLUB! I WANT TO BE WITH YOU!!!!"

Then she began to sob, and I do mean sob. Not sniffle or cry or get misty. This was full-blown sobbing and wailing at the top of her lungs. Then my two-year-old son started crying too. He didn't even know what he was crying about.

Nine years later she was still screaming, I was stuck on I-35 in a traffic jam, and I just snapped.

"RYLEE, STOP SCREAMING!!!" I screamed at the top of my lungs. I realize this is not effective parenting, but until shouting is outlawed I'm going to go with it. (My children had the nerve to look surprised.)

"Rylee, I'm the Mommy and we are going to go to the gym and that's that. Would you like me to stop home first for some peanut butter toast?"

"OK," she sniveled, composing herself. I gave both kids snacks and milk and drove to the gym. I dropped them off at Kids' Club, ignoring their sniffles, and headed to the treadmill completely frazzled.

I am the worst mother on the entire planet.

Then I put the Mother's Curse on Daniel. According to Bill Cosby, the Mother's Curse works something like this: "I hope one day when you grow up you have some children who act exactly like you do." I don't know what he was like as a child so my curse was: "I hope one day when you get married you will have some children who act exactly like mine!"

I finished my workout, showered, and felt more relaxed. Endorphins will do that. Tentatively, I entered Kids' Club . . .

"Mom, can you come back later?" asked Rylee. "Scooby Doo is on and it's the good one."

Really? *Really?*

LISA VS. DANIEL, ROUND 3 (TRUE PATRIOT)

Every March I get patriotic. That's because March is when I do my taxes and if I don't remind myself why I love America, I get really annoyed with how much money I have to pay to the government.

Day 1

I meet up with Daniel for my training session. "Lisa, you haven't updated your food journal."

"I'm being nationalistic and working on my taxes."

"It takes two minutes."

"I'm a true patriot."

I'm a true liar! I haven't updated the stupid f***ing food journal since I had my total self-sabotage meltdown last week. Dealing with taxes and a lecture on clean eating in the same week is really just too much for me to handle.

"Did you buy your supplements yet?"

He gave me a list of supplements to buy last week, like creatine and BCAA, but I don't want to buy them online because Henri will give me grief about using my credit card and I haven't gone to the vitamin store because I hate going to new places since I have no sense of direction and get lost in my own neighborhood.

"I'm. Working. On. My. Taxes," I say very slowly and deliberately. This is my "read between the lines" way of saying "stop bugging me."

He drops the subject. Yay!

Day 2

I try to dodge him but he's already there sweating away on the stepper. (He's training for the Texas Shredder competition.) "Lisa," he calls me over. *Oh, crap.* "Food journal?"

"Taxes."

"You can't be working on them forever."

"Fine. I'll update it tonight."

Of course I don't update it that night. I am actually working on my taxes. And if you must work on taxes, why not reward yourself with Hershey kisses, right? *Oh, God, now I really can't update that stupid food journal. I hate that thing.*

Day 3

I time it just right so I can avoid him entirely as he meets with other clients, but the ab workout takes me longer than expected, and Daniel slides into the training desk chair.

"Lisa—"

"I CHEATED ON MY DIET! OK?"

He shakes his head at me and goes back to his computer. He's not even looking at me. *Oh man, this week sucks.*

BONO HAT GIRL

It's my second training session this week. In an attempt to redeem myself in my trainer's good graces, I updated the food log. I also finally got my act together and drove to the vitamin shop and got my supplements yesterday. It was the fastest $100 I ever spent.

I warmed up on the treadmill and headed over to the trainer area, with some show-and-tell items.

"What's this?" he asks.

"The book I wrote and illustrated. For your nephew."

"Oh, thanks!"

"And I brought two pictures you might find interesting." I show him my photo-bomb picture with Arnold Schwarznegger. "Don't mind the double (triple) chin. I'll blame that on post-baby fat."

I pull out another piece of paper, but don't show him yet.

"What's this?"

"Do you like U2?"

"They're not really my thing."

"Well, I loved that band since I was twelve and I had a major crush on Bono. I always wanted to see him in concert, but it just never worked out. But then, when I was thirty-one, they did the Vertigo tour and Henri and I managed to get floor tickets. This was before I had kids and I was training for the Marine Corps Marathon, so I was in really great shape. Anyway . . .

. . . I was wearing a cowboy hat because I know that Bono likes to wear them, and I was sitting on my husband's shoulders, since Bono was on the stage way above us. Henri started walking towards the stage and all sense of decorum and etiquette went out the window. I threw up my arms towards Bono and was all, 'PLEASE!'

So he smiles at me and then slowly kneels down to me. He reaches out his hand and I reach for him but he pulls away! So I'm frustrated and he starts playing cat-and-mouse, staying just out of my reach. But then he's still and he slowly reaches towards me and clasps my hand. The crowd fades away and he pays attention to no one but me. I'm staring through his sunglasses at the bluest eyes I've ever seen and I can't breathe.

'How old are you?' Bono whispers.

But suddenly I'm rendered mute! How can I possibly tell him that I'm 31 behaving like a lovesick teenager? I just stare up and smile at him, blushing. He reaches down, takes my hat off my head and places it on his own. And he sings to me.

But my husband dropped the camera! So the next day I call into a radio station, let the DJs abuse me for awhile, and then people from all different sections of the audience email in pictures from the concert. It was the coolest thing ever."

I show him the paper. It says, "Two tickets to U2 concert: $45. Go-go boots, glittery shirt, and cowboy hat: $149. Having Bono *wear* your cowboy hat as he sings to you in front of 65,000 fans? Priceless." It has pictures from various angles of the concert and the picture of me beaming up at Bono.

Daniel arches his eyebrows and nods his head a little bit, examining the photos.

"That was the last time I felt really good about my body. I mean, it wasn't My Buffy Weight, but I felt strong. It was seven years ago. Also, I always look for an excuse to retell my Bono Hat Story."

"That's pretty cool, actually." He hands me back my pictures. "How you feeling this morning?" he asked as I typed in my code to the computer.

"Good."

"Do you have any questions about the supplements?"

"When do I get to use fat burners?"

He laughed. "Not yet." He grabs the clipboard with my workout routine.

"But I still need to lose fat, right? Won't they help?"

"Just use the Creatine and Isopure for now. I'll let you know when you're ready for fat burners. Just trust me."

Gah!

"This BCAA stuff tastes weird."

"You don't like it? Did you get the watermelon flavor one? I drink that stuff all day long."

"What does it do?"

"BCAA stands for Branched-Chain Amino Acid. Amino acids are the building blocks of protein. This helps your body recover faster from the muscle tears that happen when you lift weights. Don't worry, you'll learn to love the stuff."

"When will I love green beans?"

"That takes longer."

"The diet is kind of boring," I half mumble. "Can I eat something different?"

"No. I'm sorry, but that's the diet. The closer we get to the show the tougher the meal plan becomes, so you have to get used to boring. Also, your weight loss is going to slow down now."

My look of panic must have been pretty apparent because he added quickly, "Don't worry; you're still going to lose weight, just not as fast. The first fifteen pounds was mostly water weight and junk food. Now you're really going to burn fat and change your physique and that takes longer."

"OK."

He walks over to the cable pressdown where I injured myself two weeks ago. "Today, I just want to go through and correct your form. How does your shoulder feel?"

"It's OK now. Thank God for chiropractors," I smiled.

"Show me what you did."

I put the 60 lb. weight on and started to pull.

"Whoa! That's too heavy! You know, you can get just as good a workout with lighter weight and proper form."

I started to laugh out loud.

"What?" he was totally confused.

"That's exactly what my husband said. Like, *exactly*. He's been right about everything so far."

Daniel started to laugh. "Oh, you can't tell him I said that or you'll never live it down."

"I know."

He put 40 lb. on and made sure my back was aligned correctly. "You're getting a lot stronger."

"That Creatine works fast, huh?"

"It's not even in your system yet. This is just you. I checked your food log. You went off a little last week, but you're back on track. I'm proud of you, Lisa."

I smiled. I felt kind of proud of myself too.

PUSH-UPS

My favorite purchase from the San Diego Rock 'N' Roll marathon was a pink T-shirt that says "My sport is your sport's punishment." As in, the coach makes you run a lap if you're a smart-ass in class. But gym teachers could take a lesson about real punishment from the Marines. Their punishment of choice? Push-ups.

Think about it. How many military movies have you seen where some drill sergeant says, "Drop and give me twenty!" Soldiers know a thing or two about how to make people hurt.

My fear and loathing of push-ups started in high school. Gym was never fun. I was in all the geeky AP classes and had no coordination whatsoever. I felt as self-conscious and embarrassed next to the jocks as they felt next to me in English Lit.

Every year we had to take the Presidential Physical Fitness Test, only I went to Catholic school so they thought of new and creative ways to make this ordeal even worse. They combined this tribulation with introducing us to ROTC and had local Marines administer the test to us.

And I never got the cute marine, either. I always got the 45-year-old career Marine that smelled like Lucky Strikes and looked like he could kill me in about 15 seconds just for shits and giggles.

"Ladies," shouted the scary drill sergeant. "The year is 1990. There is no such thing as a 'ladies push-up!' You will do as many push-ups as you can when I say go." He held up a stopwatch. We got on the overly polished gym floor on our hands and feet and looked at the soldier in frightened anticipation.

"Go! Do you think that is a push-up? Move! Move! Move! Get lower. Nose to the ground! Do you think you're done? I've got forty seconds left on my stopwatch. Don't even think of stopping!"

Other 15-year-old children collapsed around me. I was too scared to stop. The push-up examination completed, I fell to the floor wondering how long I would have to be here until I could escape to AP History class.

"You!" He was pointing at me. Oh God, why is he pointing at me? My entire body flushed crimson. Please don't kill me scary Marine. Please don't make me do more push-ups.

He walked over to me in stern strides. His body was so erect there seemed to be a rod up him. Everyone in 5th period gym class was looking at me now. I was on the floor panting. He was nine feet tall.

"How many push-ups did you do, young lady?"

He's gonna kill me! He's gonna make me drop and do 20 more in front of the entire school! Oh why didn't I lie and get a doctor's note that excused me from gym?

"Um, fourteen . . . sir?"

His face broke into a broad smile and he gave me a thumbs up. "Good job!"

And here I am today in the gym with Daniel and he wants me to do something called "push-ups until failure." I thought failure was a bad thing?

"You do as many push-ups as you can and then stop when you can't do any more," he said.

I hate push-ups. I hate chest/shoulder/triceps day.

He demonstrates as though it is the easiest thing in the world. I am dubious. I get on the floor and balance on my hands and toes and press down.

"Your form is wrong. Bring back your arms. Raise your back. Think about it: a push-up is just a moving plank, right?"

This did not make me feel better. No wonder I hate planks: they are just stationary push-ups. A drop of my sweat falls to the floor. He's trying to adjust my shoulders but then my hips go down and I am a clumsy mess. I can't even do one push-up right.

"Let's do a modified push-up. Put your knees down."

I am shocked. *What would scary Marine think?* The push-ups are not getting any better. I'm not going low enough. I feel off balance, like I'm going to fall.

"Lisa, what are you afraid of?"

"I'm going to fall and bust my face open and you're going to laugh."

"I would probably be more concerned that you injured yourself." This made me feel better. At least he won't laugh as I break my nose falling on the floor.

"If you feel like you're going to fall, just turn your face. Try it." I do. It's not so bad, I guess.

"I can't wrap my mind around doing something to failure."

"That's the only way to test your limits and push past them." I do five. He smiles. "Good job."

Oorah, Lisa!

YOUR PROTRUDING STOMACH

Today I'm on my own. It's upper body day. Daniel is training some woman with brown hair and she is doing squats. I'm doing that amazingly annoying crossover machine that I can't seem to figure out. You start by facing the machine and grabbing the straps and then you twist in and magically are now supposed to be facing the machine with the straps crossed in front of you.

Somehow I always get tangled, which is the case today. If the weight is at 13 lb. it's just too heavy to twist, but when I try to adjust the weight, the strap snaps back and I jump out of the way because the damned thing is about to knock me out.

"Dance into it," he calls to me. *Oh! Right!* I turned the wrong way. OK . . . now the X is where it's supposed to be.

"Thumbs out." I move them. "Out. NO, OUT."

The strap goes flying and the squat client probably thinks I'm the biggest idiot on the planet. Daniel shakes his head and stifles a laugh. "I'll text you," he says and then moves his client to the safety of a machine far, far away from the likes of me.

I lower the weight all the way down to 7 lb. and still can't figure the freakin' thing out, but Daniel seems thoroughly engrossed with having the lady do hack squats now, so I move real stealthily to another piece of equipment and hope he doesn't notice.

The rest of my workout proceeds without drama and I update the weight increases in my notebook. Ah, shoulder press, the last exercise. Yahoo! He wants me to put the weight at level three but holy crap that's heavy so I reduce it to two and even that's a struggle.

I wish I could fast forward to when I'm lean and strong and don't feel so clumsy. Kind of like when it's your first day at work and you see the guy holding the cup of coffee with the Barack Obama picture on it that says, "Chill the F*** Out, I Got This," and everyone says, "Hi Bob," to him, and you want to fast forward to when *you're* Bob and can carry witty mugs and know cool things like the secret trick to make the Xerox machine work and stuff.

"Lisa."

"Huh?" I look up from my mental ramblings. Daniel's at the trainer's desk and he nods his head for me to come over.

He knows I lowered the weight. Shit!

"I spoke to a trainer friend about your protruding stomach."

OK. Mind f*** right there. I don't know if I should focus on his attempt at being tactful about describing my pot belly or on the fact that it is so problematic he feels the need to seek outside counsel to fix it.

"It's genetic," I say feebly. You see there are many shapes a person can be. There are apple shapes, where the person is chubby above the waist. There are pear shapes, where the person has thunder thighs and a big butt. My shape? Bun-in-the-oven.

Yes, I'm *that* person. I'm the woman who looks pregnant but is really just fat.

I can tell he's about to tell me that's an excuse so I cut him off. "Seriously, it's genetic. My Uncle Carl looked like he had a basketball under his belly. People used to say, 'Hey Carl, when's the baby due?'"

Now Daniel looks nervous. That's an expression I've never seen cross his face before. Uh oh.

I think my ancestors, the Vikings, must have stored excess fat in their bellies to last the long journey overseas to distant lands to raid and pillage, and my body never got the tweet that it's a new millennium and the only place I want to store fat is the fridge and not my body.

"I want you to _____." And then he tells me this top secret trick that I'd write about, but I can't, because he said I can't write about it.

"Wait—what?!" I said too loudly. Again people look at me. I am quite the spectacle today.

"Shh! Keep your voice down. I want you to _____. You don't have to do it."

"Are you kidding? Let's get rid of my pot belly!" Truth is, I love randomly weird shit like this. I love bodybuilding. This is the strangest, coolest sport ever. Plus, I've been riding that 131 to 130 scale number all week, and it's pissing me off. It will be symbolic to cross into the 120-something area, don't you think?

"You have to be careful, though. Do some research online. I just want to remind you to suck in your stomach."

"I'll be careful. Only—where do I get it?"

"I don't know. I'll ask my friend."

"OK." I start taking of my gloves, getting ready to go with newfound energy.

"You can't blog about it."

Oh man!

"You can't give away all my secrets or else why would anyone need to hire me?"

Oh great, he pulls the whole this-is-my-livelihood card on me.

"OK. No blog post. But when I write my memoir, I'm totally putting this in!"

Now it's his turn to roll his eyes at me. "OK, Lisa."

I can tell he thinks I'm never going to write the book. I'm so going to write this book. After I figure out where to buy a _____.

DUMB SHIT I SAID TO MY TRAINER (DSST): DARTH VADER MADE ME DO IT

Dave and Lucrecia (the ones we celebrated Texas Independence Day with) invited us over for a barbeque, but that means being surrounded by alcohol, burgers, and chips, and that's just too much for me to be around right now. Plus, I already got called out for cheating on my diet the last time we hung out, so I don't want a repeat of that.

The kids are bouncing off the walls, and in my attempt to start sorting through the closets I've stumbled upon an old VHS tape of *Star Wars.*

I haven't seen that movie in years. Henri and I aren't sure if the kids will be scared by it, but I recall seeing it in the movie theater when I was three and was relatively unharmed by the experience (relatively . . .) so we decide to put the tape in and get the kids sprawled out in the Man Cave (that's fancy for Henri's TV room).

Henri starts making the popcorn (not on my diet) But am I eating it? No. See? I'm being a good girl and drinking my protein shake.

Hot, salty, buttery popcorn aroma fills the air. I watch it go past me in those cute popcorn buckets to my children and husband. *Protein is good for me. Salty, buttery popcorn is not, especially when I'm going to stand onstage in a bikini in a few months.* But I feel the lure of the dark side. **YOU JUST *CAN'T* WATCH *STAR WARS* WITHOUT POPCORN, RIGHT???** It's *STAR WARS* for Pete's sake! And you can't have popcorn without Diet Pepsi, right?

I start munching and Henri starts singing, "Ooooh, I'm going to text your trainer . . ."

My cell phone goes off. *Oh shit! It's Daniel! Damned Jedi Knight; he knows! How does he do that?*

Daniel: Can you do 8-9? (For our next training session)
Lisa: 8 works
Daniel: Did u lift today?
Lisa: Yes. Chest/tri
Daniel: Perfect. So legs tomorrow and then back weds
Lisa: K. C u then. ttyl
Daniel: U stay away from BBQ?

La, la, la, la, la. It's impolite to text with your mouth full of popcorn and soda, so I watched the movie pretending to not see the message. I mentioned in passing that we were invited to the party. Figures he'd follow up on that.

But after the movie I felt kinda guilty for ignoring the text. Kinda bloated from popcorn and soda too. I look at my phone. I should probably text back. . . but it's really late and the dark side of the force is telling me to just keep it secret.

The next day I look at the phone. I consider saying nothing, ever, but he's going to call me out because he knows when I cheat, and I'm a really terrible liar. (I need to work on that.) Deciding it's better to get in trouble over the phone than in person, I text him back.

> **Lisa**: Avoid BBQ? Yes. Popcorn and Diet Pepsi, not so much. Don't worry I will do cardio penance today.
>
> **Daniel**: Lisa . . . I'm not a miracle worker. Ur diet is going to get cut drastically. Cardio will not cure things; trust me I screwed myself thinking it would.
>
> **Lisa**: It's just a one-time thing. See, we showed the kids *Star Wars* for the first time last night.

That was a totally valid excuse. Darth Vader made me do it.

> **Daniel**: So showing them *Star Wars* is going to make it right?

Uh oh, here it comes.

> **Lisa**: No, of course not.
>
> **Daniel**: Do u not remember how hard you worked last month? I'll check your diet and see but I think I have u on a good amount of food. It's a mind game. If u keep slipping up you are going to have to eat a lot less before the show.

Maybe I was wrong about it being easier getting in trouble over the phone. This sucks too.

> **Lisa**: I know.

See, the problem with the Darth Vader defense is that I was raised on the **real** *Star Wars* of 1977. So when I hear *Star Wars*, I think, "Luke, I am your Father," and "Feel the Force Around You." Daniel is in his 20s, so when he hears *Star Wars* he thinks Jar Jar Binks. I believe Urban Dictionary defined Jar Jar Binks best as: "The most hated Star Wars character ever. Far more annoying than the Ewoks because he is basically useless, and he speaks in Ebonics."

And another thing about the real *Star Wars*: Hello? Harrison Ford in his prime? If couples played the Celebrity Circle game I told you about earlier, back in 1977 (which they probably did, as there were hippies everywhere, and AIDS wasn't discovered yet), I can guarantee that Harrison Ford made it into quite a few Celebrity Circles.

Oh wait, Daniel's still yelling at me.

Daniel: I'm sorry Lisa but u have to shape up . . . I'm not a miracle worker.

Ouch! BUT DARTH VADER MADE ME DO IT!!!

Lisa: I know. I'll eat clean from now on.

Daniel: OK . . . C u tomorrow

Lisa: K . . . sorry

Daniel: You're stepping onstage not me. I can only give u the information

Damn, I've been served. Again. Stupid Star Wars. I hate that movie!

ICE BALL

My one blogger friend, Kelli, clued me into Facebook Pages. You set one up and you can link your blog posts to it, generating new traffic to your site. Once you get 30 "Likes," Facebook will give you analytics so you can see how many people read your stuff. I set my Facebook page up as www.facebook/ShesLosingIt.net/ but now I'm totally stuck. I don't know how to get my "friends" from my personal Facebook account (all six of them), to "Like" my page. But since almost 100 random people are following my blog now, how hard could it possibly be to get 30 likes on the Facebook page, right?

Kelli said to just be myself and create interesting taglines so people will want to open the links. I can be interesting. No pressure there at all. Moving on . . .

Last night we went to the Ice Ball, a fund-raiser for Big Brothers Big Sisters. Oh, it was so much fun! Anytime I get to purchase and wear a fancy schmancy dress is a good day in my book. I bought an icy-themed dress in sparkly blue for $28 from Kohl's. LOVE that store!

On the drive to downtown, Henri is all smiles and traces a finger up my thigh. "You look beautiful," he says.

We were guests of Dave and Lucrecia. His company is a corporate sponsor for the charity. There are a lot of good things about going to a charity event:

1) You are giving to a great cause.
2) Above mentioned fancy-schmancy dress.
3) Seeing various friends.

Downside to going to a big event . . . being three months out from your bikini competition and surrounded by FOOD, FOOD, FOOD you can't eat.

Exhibit A: Alcohol. This actually was not so hard for me to pass on, as I have gone through two pregnancies, so I'm totally cool going sans-alcoholic beverages for months at a time. Here's what I drank instead: Water with lime so it looked like an alcoholic beverage. OK, I'm totally lying. I had like four Diet Cokes. (Please don't tell my trainer.)

The food stations were filled with delicious things I could not eat: brisket, quesadillas, mac 'n' cheese, cheeseburgers, things wrapped in bacon, chips with guacamole, etc., etc. The healthiest thing I could find was a mini-salad of sorts comprised of a tomato slice, avocado slice, feta cheese crumbles and some bacon crumbles on top. They also had plates of a single scallop on top of some vegetable thing.

So I had two scallops and two of those tomato things for meal #5. The entire time I was eating this I was hearing Daniel yell at me in my head. ("Why didn't you follow the meal plan? I *specifically* wrote 'no tomatoes' for meal #5. CHEESE?!? BACON?!?!!!! Lisa, you're only three months out. . .")

My friend, Gayle Stallings, was the auctioneer and it was so exciting to see her in action (and get Daniel's voice out of my head). In 20 minutes she got the group to donate over $100,000! Then she continued with the live auction and brought in an additional $83,000. That woman has mad skills. (She can be found at FUNauctions.net.)

Gayle told me, "I love reading your blog! You know it's going to get turned into a book, right? It's inspiring to see that you're a mom and you can do it, so other people will think they can do it too. And I love your fights with Daniel."

What? I was so not expecting her to say that, but how great! I forget that people actually read my blog. Mostly I feel like it's an online journal just for my own amusement. I forget that I started it for a reason. . . . Anyway, I am trying to coax her into writing a guest blog post about fund-raising for sports charities. We'll see . . .

TROUBLE OVER THE ICE BALL COMETH

So, on Sunday I decided to write a blog post about the Ice Ball fund-raiser. The post really had more to do with cheating on my diet than anything else. The whole time I was writing it I was singing in my head—la, la, la, la, la—to drown out Daniel's voice. To put this in perspective, last month when I cheated on my diet, I *seriously* CHEATED (the time I pigged out on grilled cheese around weigh-in #2). This Ice Ball cheating was mostly comprised of eating the wrong type of vegetables and an unapproved protein. And, I totally DID NOT eat the chocolate-covered strawberry. I brought it home and gave it to the babysitter. Go me! Still, Daniel has a very loud voice. At least it's very loud in my head.

I posted the blog to my new Facebook page with a smart-ass little lead-in that went: "Is it possible to eat clean when you're at an event? (If you are my trainer, please don't read this.)" Totally funny, right? Since Sunday is my off day from training, and I just did my blog for the day, I proceeded with important things, like taking a nap.

Well, guess who read it?

2:25 p.m. Daniel: 9 am tomorrow? (For our training session)
2:28 p.m. Lisa: 6:30 p.m. I thought. Rylee's not in school till Tues.
2:30 p.m. Daniel: Okay that's right
2:28 p.m. Lisa: C u then!
2:31 p.m. Daniel: **And u better do cardio today bc of what u ate last night**
2:31 p.m. Lisa: Oh shit! U read tha? OK, ima do cardio
2:32 p.m. Daniel: U can't cheat
2:32 p.m. Lisa: I know
2:32 p.m. Daniel: Yeah . . . When u say "if you're my trainer don't read this" that just makes me want to read it.

Okay, in my defense here: (1) I'm trying to get to the magical 30 "Likes" on Facebook, so it needs to have an interesting lead-in for people to open the link, right? (2) Daniel is on Facebook **NEVER**. Figures this was the one day he decided to troll the web.

The next day, he still wouldn't let up. I did my cardio warm-up followed by light weights to get the blood flowing in my arms before we started our session. As I pull down the 70 lb. lat bar Daniel says, "So how were those scallops?"

Oh shit. Guess we're revisiting this . . .

"Um . . . good." He adds more weight. (Have you noticed that he likes to add more weight to whatever I'm lifting before he lectures me? This is a recurring trait of his.)

"I'm angrier about the Diet Cokes than anything else. *Four* Diet Cokes, Lisa? Really?"

"Oh, but the glasses were really small . . ." I release the bar to demonstrate with my hands. just how miniscule indeed the glasses were.

"Don't try to justify it."

"OK, sorry."

He's mad about the Diet Cokes because I'm supposed to be drinking a gallon of water a day, but I really hate the taste of water, so I've been sneaking Diet Cokes instead and hoping he doesn't notice them on the food journal. But of course, he reads that too.

So, no more Diet Cokes for me. And I will have to strategically plot the next time I write, "If you're my trainer, don't read this" for some post that totally panders to him. Or maybe I'll write that lead-in on **every** Facebook post so he'll get overwhelmed and not read any of them. Of course, the simplest solution is to just not cheat on my diet, but where's the fun in that?

POSITIVE REINFORCEMENT

Today, we are using positive reinforcement. I read all about it on the web.

The other day Little Henry saw one of those motorized cars in Walmart and was begging for it. I noticed that they had the advertisement totally wrong, listing it for $45 instead of $95, so I pounced on the opportunity. I brought the car and the signage up to the customer service desk and was all prepared to go "FALSE ADVERTISING!" on her ass if she didn't give it to me for that price, but she was totally cool and gave me the price without fuss and then ripped up the sign.

Once home, I put the car within Little Henry's sight, but totally out of his reach, and told him if he wanted the car he would have to use the potty all week.

Well guess who started using the potty?

I'm so smart. Score 1: Mom.

At the end of the week Big Henri charged the car and Little Henry zoomed all over the house. Rylee wanted to know why she didn't get a cool toy even though she used the potty every day. After I finished explaining to her all about positive reinforcement and such, I looked down to discover Little Man naked from the waist down and a puddle next to the new car he was now bored with.

"Ize a baby," he said, "I no use potty. I use diapers."

I'm so dumb. Score 1: Toddler.

ATTACK OF THE KILLER CABLES

Today is chest/triceps day and I'm already in a great mood. Why?

"I'm one hundred twenty-nine pounds! I finally broke past the one hundred thirties!" I exclaim to Daniel.

"That's great!" He gives me a high five. You would think with this grand news we would celebrate with an easier workout. Not so, my friend, not so.

We start in the trainer area so he can show me this kettlebell Tabata exercise. Kettlebells look like bowling balls with a handle.

Tabatas can be done with any exercise, not just kettlebells. The Japanese Olympic skating team developed it. Basically, you do an exercise for four minutes but you split up the intensity. You do the exercise for 30 seconds and then take a break for 10 seconds and repeat this process until four minutes are up. Apparently it burns fat hours later.

About a minute into it Daniel asks me, "How you feeling?"

"Fine." This was no big whoop.

"Uh huh. Wait till I ask you on minute three. Rest for ten seconds."

I'm using the 36" jump box (plyo box) as my mini-table to hold the kettlebell, my water bottle and my towel. I guess I'll get a drink now, I'm a little thirsty.

"Go."

Or not. I can wait 30 seconds. I'm breathing heavier. My biceps are beginning to burn a little. I look at him, waiting for him to call rest.

"Halfway."

Is he sure about the time? Because it really seems like this has been longer than 15 seconds!

"Lift higher. Above your head."

I want my water . . .

"Rest."

I gulp as much BCAA water as I can.

"Go."

Go? How can 10 seconds feel like one second and 30 seconds feel like an hour? What sort of samurai warrior bullshit is this?

"Go, Lisa!"

Sweat is trickling down my back and face and I it rub it on my arm as I lift the kettlebell above my head. My arms are shaking now as I struggle to complete the set. He's staring at the timer clock on the wall.

"Rest."

Watermelon flavored BCAA water never tasted so good to me.

It just continues on in this manner until he finally says, "Go! This is your last set. I told you these sucked."

I'm gripping extra hard onto the kettlebell handle. I have visions of it slipping out of my hand, knocking someone out, and getting sued for millions of dollars I don't have.

"Done."

I drop the kettlebell and squeeze my biceps to try to put out the flames inside them. Thank God that torture is over.

We move onto cable flyes. I sit on the chair facing the machine. He adjusts the arms of the machine so they are about shoulder height. My arms are spread wide. I'm supposed to grip both handles and pull my arms together so my hands are almost touching. This is beyond my skill set.

"Lisa, it's not brain surgery; you're pulling cables together. Stop over-thinking it."

"But that's what I do."

"Grab one handle at a time and then pull. There you go. You're doing twelve."

"When I was in high school chemistry we had to write out a formula explaining how we got our answer. My friend Carole's explanation started at the top and went down in perfect, logical order. I got the same answer but my formula was written in this weird circle. It was interesting to actually see first-hand what the inner workings of my mind looked like. It explains a lot."

"Ten, eleven, twelve. Yes, it does. Rest."

I let go and the cables go flying.

"Whoa! One at a time!"

"Sorry!"

He increases the weight, moving the peg on the next level of the weight plates.

"So, you're high school reunion's in Jersey, right?"

"Yeah."

"Grab the cables. ONE. AT. A. TIME. Good. Twelve again. But weren't you in California?"

"I was born in New Jersey, went to college in Pennsylvania, went backpacking through Europe, studied at Goldsmith College for a year—which is part of the University of London—finished school, got cast in back-to-back national tours playing Scout in an adaptation of *To Kill A Mockingbird* and then Anne Frank, moved to New York City, then moved to L.A. By the time I was twenty-five I had been to about forty-two states, and over a dozen countries, and lived in some of the coolest cities on Earth."

"And now you're in Pflugerville, Texas. Rest."

"I know, right? Doesn't it sound like a Dr. Seuss book? 'All the Pflus in Pflugerville . . . '"

"But how did you get *here*?" He adds the peg to a heavier weight.

"Well, my husband and I met in L.A. and bought a fixer-upper house together. We renovated it every weekend. After we got married, I moved to San Diego, where he lived, and we sold the house. We have a real estate guardian angel and sold it just before the market crashed. We made a pretty good profit."

"That's lucky." He hands me the cables.

"I know! I worked until Rylee was two, but I just wanted to be a stay-at-home mom, so we decided to move somewhere more affordable, and we stumbled upon Austin, Texas. We used the money as a down payment on our apartment building and on our house in Pflugerville. Two months after Little Henry was born we moved here, without knowing a soul. Kinda crazy, huh?"

"Rest. You like it here?"

"I love it here. California was so expensive and we were in an area that was very affluent and superficial. I saw seven-year-olds in hundred-dollar jeans texting people. What the hell is a seven-year-old going to text about? *Dora the Explorer*? Plus no one had a backyard. I want my kids to be able to ride their bikes in the neighborhood and be OK with hand-me-down jeans, you know?" I take a sip of water. "And you? Did you always live in Austin?"

He said a few years ago he lived in some part of Texas I'd never heard of, and when I asked why he lived there he laughed. "A girl."

"But now you're here."

"It didn't work out. I also lived in Houston and Louisiana for a while. My brother still lives in Louisiana. Grab the cables. We're only doing eight this time."

I reach for them, but I don't think I'll be able to pull both at the same time. "It's really heavy, Daniel."

"I'll help you."

Darn. I was hoping he'd just lower the weight.

"I came out here on a baseball scholarship—that's one—but I wasn't good enough to go pro."

"Oh. I'm sorry."

"Two. Don't be. It's just the truth. That's why I started doing bodybuilding. I'm pretty competitive and wanted to try another sport. I also did football when I was younger. Four. Come on, you can do this. I was the Captain of the football team and they all voted for me to come back. I'm pretty good at reading people. Six." He smiles at the memory and supports my wrists as I get closer to my arms touching. I'm moving so much slower.

"I did powderpuff football once," I stammer. *This weight is really heavy!*

"Seven. Yeah? What position did you play."

"Don't laugh." My arms are shaking.

"I won't laugh."

"Tight end."

He smirks. "Eight. You're done."

My hands are sweaty, and one cable slips out of my left hand and flings back so he has to jump out of the way.

"Oh my God! I'm so sorry!" I stand up and use both hands to slide the other cable back.

"It's OK."

I sit back down, mortified I can't figure out how to walk and chew gum. "I'd probably be the kid all you football players would make fun of."

"I'd probably put down anyone who tried to make fun of you. I didn't put up with that shit on my team. " He gives me a high five. "You're done."

That makes me feel better. But mostly I wish it's three months later when conceivably I will not be armed and dangerous with the cable machine.

FIRST DATE

St. Patrick's Day is always held dear to my heart not only because I'm Irish but also because it marks my first date with my husband. We had met six months earlier when I was 25 and had first moved to Los Angeles, but I was having far too much fun being single and going on auditions to really pay him much attention. He was just coming off a slew of bad relationships with overly needy/jealous women so it must have been novel for him to be completely ignored by someone.

In that time period, I discovered that California men were not really men at all but textbook examples of the "Peter Pan Syndrome." Coming from the east coast where men dressed for Wall Street, this never-ending childhood thing completely threw me off. After six months of this, I turned to the universe for help. This was my prayer:

> Universe, oh Universe, please send me a **man**. I'm so tired of dating boys who are pushing 30 and play more video games than the kids I babysit. Please send me a man who has discovered that sneakers, baseball caps, and sport jerseys are not the only clothing options available to men. A man who has a car would be preferable to the guys here who skateboard everywhere. Please send me a man who has a job. The boys I date seem to be incapable of keeping one (even though I have three). A sense of purpose and direction would be a nice change from the boys here whose favorite catchphrase is 'Whatever.' Amen.

No sooner did I finish my prayer when the phone rang. "Hi! Do you know who this is?"

"No," I giggled.

"This is Henri. Do you have any plans for today?"

"No," I replied.

"Yes, you do. You're going on a date with me."

Bravado. I like it.

We went to a Mexican restaurant because nothing says "St. Patrick's Day" like a taco. I was used to dating starving actors, so before I ordered I asked, "The meal I want to order is fourteen dollars. Is that OK?"

He was used to dating gold diggers, so he replied, "I love you." That was 12 years ago. We've been together ever since.

Every year we celebrate our first date anniversary by going to a Mexican restaurant, but this year I can't because I'm on the Bikini Diet and Daniel will kill me if I go off it again. Even though I totally lie to him about how often I cheat on it, he knows . . .

Our friends from L.A., Patrick and Jane, and their two kids are with us for five days. They are both utterly impressed by my weight loss and commitment to exercise. The last time they saw me I was pregnant with Little Henry. (FYI—Little Henry is really Henry Traugott V, so as a baby we called him "Fiver" because Henry was too big a name for a baby. Patrick has been calling little Henry "Cinco" all day and it's confusing the hell out of my son.)

Jane just had Brody nine months ago. You would never know she had ever been pregnant . . . twice! She is tall and lean and eats McDonald's for breakfast, which makes me jealous beyond belief. By contrast I am short, it is painfully apparent I have birthed some babies, and I have to work out twice a day and measure my lettuce to fit into my size 5 jeans.

We head downtown to show them the Texas State Capitol and 6th Street. Their son Kyler wears a shirt that says, "Kiss Me, I'm Awesome" and we all don various shades of green. South By Southwest (SXSW) is in full swing and the city is perfectly mobbed. I did not precook and pre-pack my food as Daniel suggested, because who has time for that? But I am at peace with myself because while everyone else was sleeping, I was up at 5 a.m. and working out.

But now it's 2 p.m., the kids are ready to melt down, all the restaurants have hour-long waits, and I'm starving. Plus, Henri is in a bad mood because he and the guy who works for us are in an argument on the phone. These are not the anniversary memories I want.

We finally get into a place called Wholly Cow but they don't serve salad and I can't eat burgers, so we beg and plead and they throw together some lettuce and shredded chicken in a bowl for me and call it a day. Mission accomplished. I am eating healthy.

We go home and everyone takes a nap except me. I go to the gym. Daniel is there, of course, working out with a friend. I say hi and he almost bites my head off. I mentally forgive him for this because he's only a few weeks away from his competition, The Shredder, and his coach just cut his carbohydrates, making him unbelievably grumpy. I wonder if I'm going to get grumpy the closer I get to my own completion? It's helpful to know that everything I'm going through he is too. Well, not every everything. I mean, his start point is coming from being an athlete and mine is from being a couch potato, and I doubt he ever had to deal with an error message on a pregnancy test, but it's kind of difficult to wimp out on my exercise calendar when I see him grunting away every day between clients. I like that he's living the lifestyle he preaches.

So, I'm not going to let Daniel's irritable mood rain on my parade. I'm too proud of myself for sticking to my diet and going to the gym twice today. I send Henri a text.

Lisa: Happy 1st Date Anniversary. I love you.

I come home and Patrick says, "Uh oh. Here comes Trouble. Look at the Workout Queen." This strikes me as funny and I'm happy to find someone else in a good mood. We told him about our anniversary date and he and Jane have decided to make us tacos for dinner.

While everyone else eats the real stuff, they make a special taco for me. They measure out three ounces of chicken, shred it, cook it on the Lean Mean Grilling Machine and then wrap it in a big lettuce leaf for me, and I eat the quinoa I'm supposed to from the diet.

Some days are tough. Some days are good. Today was wonderful.

I WON'T LET YOU FALL

A lot of time my life is compartmentalized and my activities are separated from each other, but every now and then there is crossover in surprising ways.

Over the weekend we went to Mansfield Dam off Lake Travis with our friends Patrick, Jane, and their kids, Kyler and Brody. The sun kept playing hide and seek behind rain clouds, and a few sprinkles fell as we parked our cars in the lot. I mentally noted the slowly winding ramp that led down to the water and wondered if we would ever get enough rain to raise the lake levels back to normal. The drought's been going on for years now.

Henri pulled the red cooler toward the covered picnic table as I unfastened car seat buckles and decided to leave my sunglasses in the car. Within minutes of reaching the table, the kids discovered the bag of Tostitos and were taking full advantage of the fact that this was a picnic and special rules applied that afforded them the opportunity to eat junk food. Jane and I also made sure to add grapes and carrot sticks into the mix, but they were only eaten as an afterthought.

Jealously, I eyed the chips and made peace with the fact that grapes and water were what I "wanted" to eat. Really . . . no, I don't want to drink that cold beer that Henri, Patrick and Jane are enjoying so thoroughly. Water is awesome . . .

Henri and Patrick started walking through the trees, seeming to find the steepest hill possible to navigate toward the water. Jane and I exchanged looks.

"There's a smooth path back where we pulled in," I offered.

"No, Lisa, that's the ramp for boats. *This* is the way to go down," proclaimed my man.

"But . . ."

But my "but" landed on deaf ears and the kids were already scrambling down the rocky terrain after the men. A bunch of people were fishing at the water's edge and my daughter, Rylee, was stripped down to her American flag bathing suit in 30 seconds. My son took disrobing a step further and went totally commando, splashing into the murky lake water with wild abandon. Not to be outdone, Kyler soon shed his diaper, too, and the boys were engrossed in skipping stones across the water in their birthday suits.

The air blew cooler and it was time to vacate the water and head up the ravine. Going down had not been so hard, but looking at the steep, almost vertical climb back to the picnic area suddenly took its toll on Rylee, and she got frightened. The white rocks looked daunting and dangerous and I wished my husband had listened to me about taking the easy way down. But now there was no way back up but to climb with arms and legs, and Rylee wouldn't budge.

Patrick said, "It's not so bad. See? Kyler can do it."

Kyler is 2-1/2. Rylee is 4-1/2. This did not make her feel better.

Henri balanced our son and the beach towel in his arms and called down to us. "Just step on the little rocks, sweetheart."

The more we told her there was nothing to fear, the more frightened she got, and she began to cry. Rylee and I watched the others approaching the top of the cliff and we were still next to the lake. Henri called down in frustration, "Just carry her!"

"No," I called back. "She's four and a half and she can do this. Go ahead. I'll stay with her. There's no rush."

Everyone disappeared over the edge and it was just my daughter and me. A bird circled overhead, casting a shadow on the rocks, and I felt a few drops of rain fall on my skin. I knelt down next to her and looked into her tear-stained face.

"You're frightened?"

"Yes."

"What are you afraid of?"

"There are spiders on the rocks and they'll bite me and I'll fall and hurt myself."

"What if we step over here? I don't see any spiders here."

"No, I'll fall." She kicked her foot against the jagged boulder, staring down in the pebble-filled dirt.

"Rylee, you know what? The other day I was really scared that I would fall too. I was doing push-ups and I thought I'd fall and hurt my face but my trainer, Daniel, said he wouldn't let me get hurt and you know what? I didn't get hurt. And I'm not going to let you fall either."

Raising her blue eyes to me, she considered this. "You get scared too?" It seemed as though the thought of me being afraid of anything had never occurred to her.

"Yes. But I did it anyway, and so will you, because you can do this, Rylee. I won't let you fall."

She sniffled a little and looked uncertainly up the hill. "OK." Grasping my hand tightly she took the first step up a tall rock, not entirely convinced this was a good idea. But she kept going as I encouraged her along the way.

"You're so brave, Rylee! Look how far you've come. Almost to the top now!"

She picked up speed as her confidence grew, and suddenly we crested the top. Before we joined the others we took a minute to look down, the uneven rocks looking ominously serrated.

"Look, Rylee. You did it! You climbed the hill even though you were scared, and I'm so proud of you."

Her face shone a crooked little smile, one forever etched now on my heart, and I thought to myself: *If my four-year-old is brave enough to conquer her fears, so can I.*

SERIOUSLY, DANIEL????? SERIOUSLY?????

"Hi. You were really grouchy on Saturday," I said point blank.

"Was I?" he asked looking up from the check-in desk.

"Yes. I said, 'You look so serious,' and you growled, 'Because I'm tired!'"

He laughed. "I'm sorry I snapped at you. I'm four weeks out from competition and my whole diet got switched so I'm really irritable."

"No kidding."

I punched in my code and we started walking over to the free weights. Today was back/bicep day. Abs too, but I do abs on my own, usually after cardio. He handed me 7.5 lb. dumbbells and I started lifting while mentally ticking off my checklist: stomach in, glutes in, lead with my elbows.

"Keep your head up."

Damn! I always forget that!

He continued, "My trainer is female and she said these last four weeks of training I'm going to feel what you women feel every month. I'm real moody."

"Hadn't noticed . . ."

Nine, ten—*holy crap these weights are getting heavy*—eleven, twelve. He takes the weights from me and I drink my BCAA water.

"And *everything* is getting on my nerves! There was this guy in the supermarket who took up the whole aisle with his cart and I was ready to go off on him. I'm taking off the week before the competition because I know I'll really be in a bad mood then. I'll be eating nothing but chicken boiled in distilled water."

"Yummy," I said sarcastically.

He hands me the weights again. "Stomach in. Shoulders back and down."

"Well, please make sure you don't train me the final days before your competition because you're too cantankerous to deal with."

"Fair enough. Ten. Just two more. Head up. Eleven, twelve. Good job. How was your weekend? Did you stick to your meal plan?"

"I had an awesome weekend. Our friends Patrick and Jane came out from California and we went to the South By Southwest free concert and I didn't drink any alcohol at all at Bikini's Bar, even though it was St. Patrick's Day and we were hanging out with an Irish Marine. And I only ate a salad. Pretty good, huh?"

His jaw dropped, eyes opened wide, and he literally stepped back. **"Why would you go out to SXSW!?! Why would you go to a bar on St. Patrick's Day!?! Why would you even put yourself in that situation!?!"** His voice got a little loud, but I'm pretty sure that had more to do with his own dieting woes than mine.

"My life isn't going to stop because I'm in a fitness competition. I wanted to have a good time with my friends. Come on, Daniel, *no beer* . . . on St. Patrick's Day! And *salad* instead of junk food!"

"Just a salad isn't enough calories, plus you didn't eat protein or carbs. You need to eat what's on the diet."

"Oh, come on!" I rolled my eyes at him.

"Don't get all defensive," he said raising his hands up, as if to block my glare like a Jedi Knight blocks an oncoming lightsaber.

"I'm not getting defensive," I muttered defensively.

"Was there chicken on the salad?"

"Yes. See? I ate protein."

"You don't know how they cooked the chicken," he answered smugly.

"SERIOUSLY?!! SERIOUSLY, DANIEL?!" Now strangers were looking at us.

"They could have used a ton of butter," he said calmly with an air of superiority. "You're fourteen weeks out and you need to stick to the meal plan or you'll never be ready for the competition."

Well, if he reacts like that to salad and chicken, I'm really not going to tell him about the five Sun Chips and hummus I ate at the concert.

We moved to lat pulldowns and I decided I wasn't going to talk to him in his current state of pissiness. *You don't know how they cooked the chicken. Really? Really? I'm not even going to talk to you anymore, so there.*

He seemed to sense my agitation and then shocked the hell out of me. "All right," he said calmly, "You're fourteen weeks out; I'm going to give you a *Cheaters Weekend.*"

I perked up. "Ooh, what's that?"

"Stick to your diet for the rest of this week, all the way until Friday. Then Saturday and Sunday *you can eat whatever the f*** you want.*"

"Anything?" I asked with wide-eyed glee.

"Anything."

"Chocolate?" This couldn't possibly be true!

"Anything."

"Fried chicken?" I challenged.

"Anything."

"Pizza?" I asked.

"Anything."

"Oh my God, really? You made my week!"

My exuberance level must have frightened him because he put in a disclaimer. "OK, you can't have McDonald's or alcohol. But everything else is fair game." He then proceeded to lecture me about the evils of alcohol with respect to bodybuilding as I moved to strength rows, but then realized my eyes had glazed over like the doughnut I was thinking about. "Everything OK, Lisa?"

"Honestly, I'm not listening to you. I'm thinking about the chocolate Easter bunny I'm going to buy at HEB after we're done here."

I Opened the Door and In Flu Enza

"I get a Cheater's Weekend!" I declared upon entrance to my guest-filled house.

"What's that?" asked Henri, visibly concerned about my excitement level.

"I get to eat," and then I lowered my voice to a hush since little people were present, "whatever the f*** I want!"

"That's awesome!" said Patrick.

"Why would you do that?" asked Henri slowly.

"Because it's a Cheater's Weekend!"

"You finally got down to a size five. Why on earth would you eat crap all weekend and gain all the weight back?" he said.

"Don't rain on my parade. I'm hungry. I haven't eaten junk food in six weeks. I'm sick of tilapia. I'm sick of quinoa. I'm sick of green beans, and my trainer said I can eat whatever I want, so I'm going to."

"I've been in agreement with pretty much everything your trainer said up until now. But I think it's a mistake."

"Well, you're not my trainer, so back off."

"Does anyone want coffee?" asked Jane, trying to tactfully switch subjects.

We should not be fighting in front of them. I should have never told Henri about Cheater's Weekend. Now he's going to be a pain in my ass about it all week, I can tell. Thank God I left the bag of chocolate deliciousness in the trunk of my car. Here's what I bought:

1. Peter Rabbit chocolate Easter bunny
2. Cadbury Eggs
3. Hostess cupcakes (8 pack)
4. Diet Coke
5. Tostitos
6. Salsa
7. Bacon
8. Sharp Cheddar Cheese

I probably will get some more things too. I want to make crepes, and eat fried chicken, and have Henri make his homemade macaroni and cheese and also his potato tacos. I also want to eat Indian food and lasagna and lobster bisque at the Cajun restaurant. Maybe I'll get more cupcakes; I'm not sure eight will be enough. It's only one weekend so I'll have to make the most of it.

Jane and Patrick go upstairs with Henri to get their suitcases to go home today. I race to the car and sneak the food in before anyone notices.

Jane is collecting the boys. Little Brody does not look well.

"He's been up all night with a fever," she said.

Poor little thing. Before they leave she hands me a gift.

"What's this?" I ask.

"Well, you said the soap at the gym dries your skin, so I got you some body wash for your gym bag."

"Oh thanks!"

We hug. Patrick congratulates me again for losing the weight.

"Enjoy your Cheater's Weekend," he whispers, "you've earned it."

I smile. After they leave, I notice that Rylee isn't nearly as rambunctious as usual, but chalk it up to her winding down after the excitement of having guests for a week.

The next morning I head over to the gym with my sweatshirt on. I'm walking on the treadmill, next to Crew Cut Treadmill Guy, and watch Pink Hair Lady do mountain climbers on the machine in front of me. Suddenly, I'm seeing black spots in front of my face. I hold on to the rails and try to continue but my breathing is getting shallow. I stop the machine and grab the disinfectant to wipe it down so I don't spread germs. It's hard to breathe, so I go in the locker room and take off my sweatshirt. I splash cold water on my face, but now I'm shivering. I put my wet sweatshirt back on and head to the car. My phone is buzzing.

6:52 a.m. Daniel: Don't hold the rails!

6:57 a.m. Lisa: I'm sick. I don't think we can meet tomorrow. Should I do something on my own?

6:58 a.m. Daniel: No. If you're sick, just rest.

6:58 a.m. Lisa: I don't want to mess up my schedule.

6:59 a.m. Daniel: You have time. Feel better.
7:00 a.m. Lisa: K

I go home to the pea soup scene from *The Exorcist*. Both kids plus Big Henri are ferociously ill and guess who gets to clean up all the vomit? I clean up the bathrooms and head to CVS to buy saltine crackers and Gatorade. I'm sick too, but just fever and achy; the contents of my stomach are intact.

The week progresses and Big Henri gets worse. He jokes that this was a secret ploy on his part to lose as much weight as me, but I'm really starting to get scared now. He was supposed to go into work to fix the two bedroom unit because the new tenant has to move in on the first, and the contractor is mad because he doesn't have the materials he needs to do the work on his own. Henri wants to go to work but I tell him I'll kick his ass if he even thinks about it.

By Friday afternoon the kids are feeling a little better. Big Henri is still sick and passes out on the floor. I wake him up, but his skin is gray and I'm beside myself with fear. I run across the street to my neighbor's and ask them to watch the kids so I can take him to the emergency clinic.

After two hours of paperwork, multiple nurses, and poking and prodding, they finally tell us that we have to go to the hospital—Henri has walking pneumonia and is severely dehydrated. On top of this, he has the nerve to tell me we can't afford a hospital bill and he wants to go home.

"ARE YOU KIDDING ME!?! WHAT GOOD IS IT IF YOU'RE DEAD!?!"

He sees that I'm serious, so he mumbles an apology and he leans over my shoulders as I walk him to the car. I drive like a mad woman.

"Henri, it's just money. You can't take it with you. We'll get through this, like everything else."

He says nothing, just stares out the window. I say a little prayer in my head.

At the hospital they hook him up to an IV and inject him with medicine. I get a text on my phone about Obamacare from some robodial and want to throw it against the wall. By 11 p.m. the color returns to his face and we head home. We thank the neighbors profusely for watching the kids and they are happy Henri is better. We are lucky to live near such good people.

CHEATER'S WEEKEND—MIDNIGHT FRIDAY

"What's better," asked Bill Maher of one of his foodie guests, "mediocre sex or a great meal?" The guest answered (and I'm paraphrasing here), "Depends who's f***ing and what's for dinner."

Cheater's Weekend officially starts tomorrow. Well, I've had one hell of a week with everyone in the household getting the flu and my husband in the hospital with pneumonia. It's midnight Friday now, so technically it is tomorrow. . . . The kids are asleep. I help Henri into bed; he's still shaky but better from the IV drip and antibiotics.

My nerves are frayed, I'm worried about Henri's health, I'm stressing about the hospital bills to come and I have to go to work tomorrow morning at 7 a.m. to help with the apartment remodel, even though I'm still sick with the flu. Perhaps this is the perfect time for Cheater's Weekend after all.

I go to the pantry and pull out the Hostess chocolate cupcakes from their hiding spot and place the package on the polished dining room table. I pour myself a huge glass of milk and sit in the quiet room enjoying my solitude.

Just as women will never fully understand why grown men love comic book heroes so much, men will never understand the near orgasmic experience women feel while eating chocolate. The first bite of cupcake is a sensual orgy for my taste buds. The chocolate is fragrant, the luscious sweetness fills my mouth and it is positively delectable. The milk complements it and I feel absolute ecstasy. There is nothing going on in the world right now; just the joy of chocolate.

That went so well I decide to open the Cadbury Eggs I purchased earlier.

Expectant of another magnificent flavor party to cross my lips I rip away the foil and bite quickly . . . only . . . it's sweeter than I remembered it being. It's too sweet, actually, it almost *sickens* me with saccharine. *Hmm. That's new.* I finish one egg but put the rest back in the pantry. Maybe they will taste better tomorrow.

Milk still tastes good and I wash out the syrupy taste. Reaching into the refrigerator, I take the Diet Coke that I so lovingly placed there this morning in preparation for Cheater's Weekend and decant it into an ice-filled glass.

Now I want salty. Pouring the salsa into my favorite bowl I lie it down on the gleaming table and open a new bag of Tostitos. Sure, there is already an open bag my husband was munching on, but I wanted a brand new bag, completely fresh and untouched. The first chips were *good*. The salt bit at my tongue and the salsa smelled divine. But after about five chips I felt full.

I wonder how much weight I'm going to gain this weekend? *Damn Henri for putting that in my mind!* He's terrified Cheater's Weekend is going to put me back into my size 14 jeans and wants me to stay on the diet. But to hell with him, I'm hungry, I've worked hard and I deserve this break.

Forcing more chips down my throat, I suddenly feel thirsty and take a sip of soda. *It tastes awful.* Wait . . . what? I check for an expiration date. *Was this sitting around too long? Why does it taste so bad?*

Maybe it needs rum . . . but that's not allowed so I just stick with the soda. I don't want any more chips so I roll up the bag and put it away and wrap up the salsa for later. Maybe my sense of taste is off from the flu?

Cheater's Weekend is not getting off to a good start. I will try to eat more crap tomorrow and feel better about it.

CHEATER'S WEEKEND—SATURDAY

Waking the next morning I feel dreadful. I haven't exercised in over a week now and my stomach is bloated and uncomfortable from last night. I step on the scale. Yesterday morning I was 127 pounds. Today I am 132 pounds. The world is a cruel dark place.

Even though yesterday it was 63 degrees, today it's 87 degrees because Austin weather makes no sense, and I dress in my ratty old construction T-shirt and shorts. Since I feel gross I eat Kashi® GOLEAN® for breakfast, which is actually pretty healthy. I feel bummed I'm wasting Cheater's Weekend on healthy food but the thought of pancakes and bacon, which is what I had planned on, nauseates me.

Brian, our Property Manager, meets me at the building. "Wow! You lost a lot of weight! You look great!"

"Thanks," I say smiling, feeling the tightness of my waist pressing against my jean shorts.

We go to unit 105 and start to work. Officially I am the boss but Brian has way more skills than me so I am the "gofer," as in, "Go fer this hammer, go fer that bucket." I demo the shower tile, which is normally pretty fun—I enjoy being destructive—but today I just feel sluggish. I'm carrying boxes of tile and dragging hacksaws back and forth. I'm on my hands and knees grouting in the kitchen and coughing up a lung. Even though I'm on antibiotics and not contagious, my chest feels weighted and I have no energy. We stop for lunch.

In honor of Cheater's Weekend my husband made me his famous macaroni and cheese, which I automatically added salt to without even tasting. I open another Diet Coke. Maybe last night's can was a fluke? It wasn't. The soda sucked. The macaroni felt like it expanded down my throat to where I was almost choking. I ate about a third of it. I didn't even want to look at it.

WHAT THE HELL?!? What's the point of having a Cheater's Weekend if everything tastes bad and I feel disgusting?!?

Ohhhhhhh . . .

DAMN YOU, DANIEL, AND YOUR STUPID JEDI KNIGHT TRICKS!!!!!!!!!!!!!

I'm sitting in my husband's truck, ready to go home for the day. I pull Peter Rabbit out of the box, the treat I've been lusting over for a week now. I eat the ears first, then the tail, 'cause that's how I roll. And then I do something I've never done in 38 years.

I throw the rest away.

I text Daniel.

5:08 p.m. Lisa: I'm ending Cheater's Weekend a day early . . . Can you please send me my new diet?
5:09 p.m. Daniel: LOL. Do you feel like crap?
5:09 p.m. Lisa: Yes.
5:10 p.m. Daniel: Good! See you on Monday with your new diet.

Sometimes I hate Daniel.

THAT WAS LAST WEEK. THIS IS TODAY.

We're at the incline bench press and I just can't lift it; he has too much weight on it.

"Come on," Daniel prods.

"I can't," I say through gritted teeth, pushing with all my might and feeling the double frustration one can only feel when the weight (a) won't budge, and (b) won't budge in front of someone.

"You're not focused today," he reprimands, taking off all the weight from the bar. I feel the need to defend against his accusation.

"Well, everything's off balance! My whole schedule has been messed up for two weeks! First Henri was in the hospital and then the kids got sick and then I got sick and I couldn't get my workouts in and now I just feel weak and like I'll never catch up."

"That was last week. This is today."

I sit up on the bench to face him (*glare at him*) and he kneels down so he's on my level.

He rubs his thumb across his bottom lip in thought. "Is Henri OK now?" he asks in a less brusque manner.

"Yes."

"Is he back to work now?"

"Today is his first day back."

"Your kids are healthy again?"

"Yes; they're in Kids' Club right now."

"And you're OK now?"

I exhale slowly, "I guess so."

"Then let it go."

"I can't. I can't just turn things off like a switch in my brain."

"That's an excuse."

"It's not an excuse, it's what happened."

"Life happens. You're going to get sick. You're going to miss workouts. If you miss one, you miss one. You can't make up for it, so you have to just move on."

I pause a little to absorb his line of reasoning. I tend to hold on to things forever; it's the historian in me. Daniel is all sports. Captain of the football team, college baseball scholarship, bodybuilder. I guess you have to let things go in sports or you would always be reliving last week's game.

Slowly I lean back on the bench and struggle to lift the bar, struggle to clear my mind of last week's setbacks. My grip on the cold metal is tight, its roughness pressed into the skin on my hands. Staring at the lights in the rooftop, I finally manage to lift.

"One," I say.

I STRETCH NEVER

Stretching should be a part of any healthy exercise routine. I know this. I've been told this . . . I've just finished doing a bazillion squats and Daniel says, "Good. Where do you feel that?"

"My legs," I answer. *Duh.*

"But which part of your leg?"

"Oh. My calves."

"Are you stretching like I showed you?"

"Uh huh," I lie.

He cocks his head and looks down at me, making me feel shorter than my 5'2" frame. Sometimes I really hate tall people. "Really?" he asks dubiously.

"I stretch never," I say, flashing an energetic smile.

"I know," he says flatly, "because if you did you would feel your quads and not your calves. When you skip stretching you can't get full range of motion."

Oh, blah, blah, blah. Stretching is time consuming.

"You need to stretch for at least ten minutes in the sauna before we train."

"Is that before or after the thirty minutes of cardio you just added?" He had recently added a 30-minute warm-up that I was supposed to complete prior to our sessions.

"After."

I'm doing mental calculations of everything I have to do. Fifty minutes of cardio in the morning followed by 16 minutes of abs (but that's up for debate—he says it should take 16 minutes but it takes me 30 minutes), then come back later and do 30 minutes of cardio plus now 10 minutes of stretching and then 50 minutes of weights and *holy hell that's a lot of time at the gym*! I must be making quite an expression on my face because he reads my mind without me asking anything aloud.

"Lisa, the closer you get to the competition the more time you are going to spend at the gym. It becomes a time management game. But you really need to stretch so you don't hurt yourself. Also, I want you to start taking weekly progress pictures of yourself in a bikini, front and back."

AHHHHHHHHHHHHHHHHH!!!!!!!!!!!

"Normal" People

The other day I was in a grumpy mood. Now it's Daniel's turn again.

Today we're doing an upper body workout that he wants me to do every Friday. This is the last exercise. We go to the assisted chin-up machine. To do a chin-up, you do a wide grip on the bars and pull yourself up until your chin is above the bar. This takes a massive amount of upper body strength; well, I guess "massive" is a relative term. If you're a dude, I guess it's no big deal really, but women find it pretty tough. An unassisted chin-up means you can lift up your own body weight. An assisted chin-up means the machine takes off a certain amount of weight to make it easier. Make sense?

Daniel puts the peg on 54. So the math equation is My Weight (127 lb.) minus 54 lb. = I'm really lifting 73 lb. And it's still not really easier. I'm struggling through these exercises, but it seems he's struggling through his own things today.

"Everything OK, Daniel?" I say during my rest.

"I don't know. I guess I'm just not used to working with, you know, *normal* people," he says looking at me.

Oh great. The first time in my life somebody calls me "normal" and it's not meant as a compliment. "Normal?"

"I'm used to dealing with college kids at UT and athletes; people who are really into it and want to do better. It doesn't matter. Go again."

"I could see how it would drive you nuts dealing with desperate housewives and middle managers all day," I said, knowing full well I'm one of them.

He changed the peg to 48, so now I'm really lifting 79 lb. and it's unbelievably difficult after the second chin-up, but I'm trying. I feel bad that he had to deal with me and all my cheating on the diet for the past two months. But I never claimed to be an athlete, or to even want to be one. I'm quiet.

I guess he's reading me now. "It's not you. I mean, you cheat on your diet, but at least you tell me about it. I have this one client and every time we get close to her goals she gives away sessions to her daughter. Her last doctor visit her cholesterol levels were down, her weight was down, her medications were reduced, and I was really excited for her. Then she stopped. You're done. The weight's too heavy for you, we're going back to fifty-four next time so your form's right."

He moves the peg and I begin chin ups again. I've had so many different personal trainers the past decade and not once did any of them mention to me their disappointment that clients weren't getting healthy. They spoke about their boyfriends or girlfriends or latest movie or complained about how little personal trainers make for a living. If they did care about their clients it was kept secret from me.

"Maybe you should be a coach? You would be good at that," I offered.

"I don't know. You're done. Good job."

I climb down from the machine and feel his critical eyes scan over my body and feel like the monster to his Dr. Frankenstein. He nods his head "yes" and wears a self-satisfied look on his face.

"You're almost twelve weeks out. Now the *real* training begins," he says cryptically.

"Real training? What the hell have the last two months been then? You mean it gets worse? How is that even possible?"

"The first two months was just a warm-up, getting your head in the game. Now we sculpt. How much cardio are you doing?"

"I'm doing forty minutes Monday through Friday plus thirty minutes on the bike before we train. Plus the stretching you just added."

"OK, we need to up your cardio to fifty minutes, plus I want you to do it on Saturdays too."

"WHAT!?! Oh my God, I'm going to LIVE at the gym? How on earth am I supposed to handle regular things like paying bills and doing laundry when you've just doubled my cardio?"

"I didn't double it. It's just an extra hour and forty minutes a week. Lisa, I told you before, from now on this becomes a time management game. You good?"

"Um . . . OK. Yeah, I'm good."

"Good." He scans the cardio equipment quickly and squints at the clock. "Where's my seven o'clock?" he mutters to himself. "She better not be late." He's walking towards the desk and texting furiously.

And I'm like . . . *Thank God, I'm not his seven o'clock.*

MOVING UP THE GYM RAT RANKS

The first hint that you are moving up the gym rat ranks is when you can identify all the tribal elders and they are willing to glance at you as you walk by. If you are sweating profusely they might even show the hint of a smile as you pass.

But you have still not earned the right to talk to them. They will keep their iPod headphones locked in their ears to avoid unwanted conversations with you.

The second hint is when the people at the front desk learn your name (and you learn theirs).

"Hi Lisa!"

"Hi Doug! Hi Kim!"

But the real sign that you are in middle ranks is when a fresh crop of newbies comes to the gym after a membership discount mailing has gone out, and they begin to ask *you* questions. (Elite Gym Rats are still too scary to talk to, but you seem like a safe bet.) They will ask you how to use the machines and why you wear a sweatshirt when you run. They will watch you when you stretch.

And then one day it happens. You are fit. You see newbies in the periphery of your vision try to mimic the ab routine on the stability ball you just completed. You go to the locker room and see an Elite Gym Rat and she takes off her headphones and talks to you for the first time.

OMG! Skinny Tan Woman is talking to me!

"I see you've been working hard," she says.

Her voice sounds nice!

"I've lost twenty pounds! My name's Lisa. I'm training for the Adela."

"My name's Obidia. I'm training for the Shredder."

So she's a bodybuilder too. She's not a scary gorilla woman at all. Ha! Henri was finally wrong about something! Score 1: Wife.

THE M&M SITUATION

When Rylee was potty training (I mentioned she did it in ten days, right?), we used The Diaper Ceremony and one other trick I've been avoiding thus far. Oh yeah. I'm bringing out the big guns: M&M's.

I bought a giant bag and placed them in a plastic jar and told Little Man I'd dole out one M&M for pee-pee and two for poo-poo. He was thrilled!

Big Henri came home and saw the jar and tilted his head to the side. *Oh great, here it comes.* A big lecture about my eating habits coupled with his complaints about my failure to potty train our son. But he didn't say anything.

But I wasn't going to let it drop, because I had already mapped out this verbal battle in my head, so I followed him to our bedroom where he changed out of his work clothes.

"The M&M's are working," I said.

"That's good," he said turning on the water in the shower. I stood there for a moment, but he didn't comment further. This annoyed me and I wasn't sure why.

"I mean, I know it's not on the meal plan or anything, but I think it's working with him. And *I'm* not eating it."

"Hey, that's between you and your trainer."

I seriously don't know how to respond to this, because I realize that I'm the one who is trying to pick a fight with my husband over my eating habits and he's not falling for it. Score 1: Husband

FACEBOOK KEEPS GETTING ME INTO TROUBLE!

New Rule: Facebook needs to create user divisions like they have in bodybuilding competitions: Facebook and Facebook for Middle-Aged+ People.

I'm sorry, but my brain can't keep up with the 12-year-olds who run the website. Every time I open Facebook my timeline has changed, stuff gets moved around, and there are new policies you need a law degree to understand. And speaking of laws, if the Supreme Court has ruled in *Citizens United* that corporations are people, why can't my FB Page get friends? Why do I have to log in as me, and then invite friends to like my page? *And by the way, how do I do this?*

Oh sure, Facebook has its place for things like assisting the manhunt to capture a terrorist, and aiding common people revolting against tyrannical leadership to form more open societies in their home countries, but what about the really important things? Like helping a middle-aged mother and novice bodybuilder grow her blog? How is Facebook helping her (me)???

Facebook and I go way back (like two months ago) when I first discovered that the "f" logo should really stand for "FU, Lisa."

As part of my efforts to get 30 likes, I've been adding funny titles to get people to click on my posts. Y'all remember how funny it was when I wrote, "If you're my trainer, don't read this," and then my trainer read it, and I got in trouble? Well, I was like, "Who cares?" because I also got 30 likes after writing that post since, apparently, you all like it when I get in trouble.

But now that I'm trying to up my game and get to that magical 100 "Likes" so I can win a set of steak knives, things have just gone crazy. Last night I just did a blog post about eating protein to build muscle mass, which had a picture of me doing a bicep curl, a picture of some eggs, and a picture of my niece's husband (who is a bodybuilder/personal trainer) with her 3-year-old daughter. Pretty noncontroversial stuff.

But I had to make that eye-catching title and tagline, so I wrote this: "Size Doesn't Matter. Unless You're Bodybuilding. Or having sex. Then it matters a whole lot." Pretty funny, right? Well, Facebook decided that the *very best* picture to use for this post was the one with my niece's toddler. OH SHIT!!!! So I deleted the post, apologized to my niece, and now I'm going to stop trying to be interesting.

To err is human. To really mess things up you need Facebook.

TRAIN TO WIN

It's leg day. I'm on the hack machine feeling pretty strong. Daniel leans on the nearby smith machine as I push off.

"One, two, three. Push through your heels. Weight OK?"

"Yes," I grunt.

"Seven, eight. We're getting closer to competition. Are you getting excited? Ten, eleven, twelve. Rest."

"I'll just be happy to walk onstage. I can't believe how much weight I lost already," I beam.

His face dropped and he leaned his jaw into his fist. *Oh no, what did I do wrong now?*

"How much weight did you lose already? Thirty-one? Thirty-two pounds?"

"Yeah, thirty-two."

"You're changing your whole life, aren't you?"

"Yeah, I guess I am." I shrug my shoulders. *Where is he going with this?*

"Why won't you train to win?" he asks quietly.

"Well, I'm never going to win, so why try? I mean, I never even *thought* about *winning* . . ."

"I know, I know, you just want a nice bikini body, and you'll have that, it's just, you're the first person I've trained for the bikini competition and I think you could maybe place if you only tried."

This was news to me on both fronts. Since he was a bodybuilder himself I just assumed he trained other bodybuilders for competition; I never thought I was his guinea pig. I keep forgetting how young he is. And he thinks I could place? Yet another sign of his youthful optimism.

"Oh, you want that trainer success story on the wall, don't you?"

"Yeah," he laughed.

"And you'll get that. I'll write something up. I think you're a great trainer. I'm more in shape now than I've ever been."

"I just think you should try. You have to train to win."

But now I feel awkward. I'm never going to win. Why would he even suggest I could?

When I get home, Henri reads my face. "What'd he call you out on now? Did you cheat on your diet again?" he asks pouring the Cheerios into Rylee's bowl.

"No. He says I'm not trying hard enough."

"Not trying hard enough? You're in the gym twice a day!"

"He said I have to train to win. He says I'm not doing that right now."

"Win? I though you just wanted to walk onstage."

"I do."

"Well don't go and get all bulky muscular on me. You look beautiful right now."

"I guess. I don't know."

Little Henry slams into my legs almost knocking me over. "Milk pwees!" he says in his cute toddlery voice. I tussle his coppery red hair. He is Velcro toddler now and attached to my thigh as I get the milk from the refrigerator.

"Don't know?" asks Big Henri, thoroughly nonplussed. "I don't want you getting big. You're doing this for me aren't you?"

I shrug my shoulders and detach Velcro toddler. "I'm taking a shower."

I peel away my exercise garb and step into the hot stream of water and begin to wash my hair. I love Henri and want to please him, but I'm not doing this for him. And Daniel is a great trainer, and I don't want to disappoint him, but I'm not doing this for him either. I'm doing this for me and truth is I don't want to fail. If my goal is to just walk onstage and look decent, then I've won.

Because if I say I want to win and then don't even place, I'll just feel bad. Won't I?

YOU'RE PRETTY

Today is leg day again. We're doing walking lunges across the floor.

It's two weeks away from the Texas Shredder and Daniel is in the leaning-out phase of his diet. Most of his carbs are cut out and the thing about cutting out carbs from your diet is it makes you pretty dippy.

"Are you OK?" I ask him concerned.

"My food intake just got cut. You know how I used to eat about four thousand calories a day? Well, my trainer just cut me down to what you're eating."

"Fifteen hundred calories a day?"

"Yeah."

"That's crazy."

"That's the sport. Go lower, knee almost to the floor."

I have a 30 lb. bar on my back and it's difficult to maintain balance. A man walks up to the water fountain and I hesitate so he can drink.

"Keep going. He can move," Daniel says loudly. The man looks taken aback, finishes his drink and moves away abruptly, wiping his mouth with his sleeve.

I wonder if Daniel is always this aggressive or if it is heightened by the restrictive diet and whatever supplements he's taking.

"Are you nervous about the competition?"

"Nervous? No, I'm excited. Dip lower. LOWER. Come on, Lisa, that doesn't even count. Do it again."

I dip until my knee touches the floor. When I rise I see the grayish black smear of dirt on it and wonder how long it will take before I reach 30 steps. Well, 31 steps I guess.

"Seventeen, eighteen. Press up from your heels. Some guys I know are dropping out already, taking more time to train."

"But you're not?"

"F*** them, I'm ready."

Despite the weight on my back I tug a smile. His twenty-something bravado is amusing.

"Twenty-eight, twenty-nine, thirty. Turn around, do it again."

I groan internally. I would groan aloud but he might take offense and increase it to 50 steps.

"You know, I think it's pretty cool you're doing this competition," he says to me. "Chest up, look ahead. I don't think you realize how much your confidence has grown. A lot of women I know train for a solid year and a half before they even consider stepping onstage. You're doing it in five months."

"Oh? People train that long?" I know nothing about this sport.

"Yeah. Fourteen, fifteen. Turn around and walk back. That's why I think it's so cool you just came in, said, 'I'm doing this thing,' and bang! You're getting it done. I brag about you to all my other clients."

I almost drop the weight.

"You do?" This is news to me. I thought he used me as a case study for what a diet cheater acts like.

"Of course. Look how hard you work. And you dropped what, like thirty-five pounds already?"

"Well, you're a good trainer."

"A trainer is only as good as his clients. Look, you're the one deciding when to eat or not eat. You're the one getting up at five and doing sprints in a sweatshirt. I just give you the tools; you do the work."

"Yeah, my sweatshirt is pretty stinky."

He tilts his head to the side and says in all sincerity, "Well, you could wash it."

Henri and I have a little inside joke. Whenever I say something he deems amusingly stupid he will pat my head and say, "You're pretty." (He says this more often than I'd like to admit.) At that particular moment I wanted to say the same comment to Daniel but (a) that would be completely inappropriate, and (b) that would be completely inappropriate. So instead I go for sarcasm.

"Really? I thought I would just never wash it again as a token of my dedication to this sport; that way people could smell me coming and be inspired." He starts laughing. "Thirty. Good job."

M&M Update

M&M rewards are working. Sort of. Only instead of taking one to two M&M's, it's more like one to two fistfuls of the candy, plus Rylee is eating them too. This means my house now has a toddler and a preschooler amped up on chocolate running around and driving me crazy. But like everything else, Little Man is growing tired of M&M's and starts handing them to me.

"You eat, Mama."

Finally, I just put a diaper on Little Henry and text Big Henri potty training is on hold until after the competition.

I'm ashamed to admit it, but I don't think I'm ready for him to stop being a baby yet, either. I cuddle him and he's just so content to be in my arms. It's not like he's starting kindergarten; he's only 2-1/2. I eat the last handful of M&M's and hug him closer.

"Ize a baby, Mama," he says drifting off to sleep.

Yes, he's my baby.

EASTER SUNDAY

Texans love them some Jesus. I'm Catholic, but Henri is Protestant, which means we went church shopping until we found one that clicked for both of us. They have mega churches here with 20,000 people stadium seating and some of the churches have bands that play the best Christian rock you've ever heard. (If you ever hear Christian rock—that is. But even if you haven't, trust me, going to church here is way more fun and emotionally moving than you'd expect.)

Last fall, when I was at my lowest point and just before deciding to enter the bodybuilding competition, we stumbled upon Austin Stone, a non-denominational church that some of our tenants attended. (They were nice people, so why not try it out?)

They had FREE childcare. OK—I was praising God just for that alone. The preacher, Matt Carter, just returned from Israel. While he was there he made a video of himself reading the most influential sermon of all: Jesus' Sermon on the Mount, verbatim, in the same location where Jesus spoke it over 2,000 years ago.

It's strange to admit, but I'd never heard the entire sermon from start to finish before that day; just segments of it. Sometimes I forget that Jesus was a real person who walked the earth. He just seems like a story in a book I listen to every Sunday.

But that day I just listened to His words and in the video they showed the Sea of Galilee and it felt like I was back in time. Struck by the beauty and poetry and simplicity of the language, an invigorated peacefulness washed over me, if that makes sense. We've been going ever since.

"So you're Protestant now?" my brother asks me on the phone.

"Um, I don't know . . ." *Back off Mr. I-Go-To-Church-Christmas-Easter!* The truth is, I don't know much about things of a spiritual nature, but I know I feel good coming to this church, so that's a start.

Normally we go to the church near the apartment building we own, but since this is Easter Sunday, they are holding the service at the Erwin Center—which is the venue downtown where rock stars have concerts when they're in town—because they are expecting over 14,000 people to attend.

I'm wearing my size 4 pale pink business skirt suit. The last time I wore it was 2004? 2005 maybe? With the skirt unbuttoned and held up by a safety pin? Today it's loose.

The kids look adorable. Rylee is in a pink ballerina dress with a fancy white hat and gloves, and Little Henry is wearing a blue shirt and tie. He looks like a little Wall Street stockbroker. I ask someone to take our family picture with my cell phone. Big Henri and I are laughing. The kids are squirming. It's not lost on me that God has answered my prayer from last November. I can't remember the last time our family was this happy.

I text our picture to Daniel.

Lisa: Happy Easter! I'm wearing size 4!!

Daniel: Congrats! You're family is gorgeous.

Lisa: Thanks ☺ And thanks for helping me lose so much weight. U r a great trainer.

Daniel: Aww. U can have 4 dark chocolate Hershey kisses today. Happy Easter.

Lisa: No way, man! I have to step onstage in a bikini in 11 weeks. Are you nuts?

Daniel: LOL! Good! I was hoping u would say that!

Lisa: ☺ TTYL

IT'S NOT JUST ME?

It's 6 a.m. and I'm on the StairMaster. Since I'm not allowed to read, and ESPN is boring, I decide to people watch. Pink Hair Lady is lifting weights in the open dumbbell area. Crew Cut Treadmill Guy is on the treadmill. Obidia (formerly known as Skinny Tan Woman) is doing lat pulldowns. She looks really good.

Daniel is in the far corner with a client, so I start watching them. The woman looks really good, but something is wrong. She has her head down and says something.

I'm trying to read lips, but my vision isn't so good. But lip reading was not required with what happened next. Daniel says real loud, "YOU DID WHAT!?!"

Oh shit! What did she do? I wrap my arms around the StairMaster monitor display and lean in closer to watch.

She's looking down, but her hands are crossed in defiance. *Oh this is getting good!* His hands are on his hips now. He's shaking his head "no."

"You can't do that. You can't do that," he says.

I know I shouldn't be watching the drama unfold. I wouldn't want other people to watch me get in trouble, but it's like a train wreck; I can't pull my eyes away. Plus, let's face it, the gym rats get to watch me get in trouble twice a week, so it's novel to realize I'm not alone. It's not just me: Daniel's tough on everyone.

She's not looking at him, but she's nodding her head "yes" now. Her hands are still crossed though. He's talking quietly. I can't make out what either of them are saying, so I lean in closer.

OH SHIT! HE'S LOOKING STRAIGHT AT ME NOW AND GLARING! I'M SO BUSTED! I stand up straight, fly my hands off the rails, and avert my eyes faster than Charlie Sheen says "winning" after doing a line of coke.

Watch ESPN, watch ESPN, watch ESPN.

Two minutes later I peek back over at them. (Train wreck. I know.) They've resolved their dispute. He holds up his hand and she gives him a tentative high five. Then he proceeds to kick her ass with a leg/glute workout from hell.

Sweat is dripping down my face just watching it. Also because the StairMaster is way harder when you're not holding the rails. *Note to self:* Do not piss off Daniel on leg day.

HEELING

Daniel wants me to go to the Texas Shredder show so I will have an idea of what to expect for my own show in June. He, as well as a group of people from my gym, will be competing. You can tell who the contestants are; they look fabulous!

One of the competitors is Chris. Remember, she was the trainer I did three sessions with in November, and who told me about the bodybuilding show in the first place, but I didn't keep training with her because I didn't want to compete against my trainer?

In typical awkward fashion I was afraid she might be mad at me, but today I saw her in the gym and she looked beautiful and just so happy, so I went up to her.

"You look great!" I said.

"I lost six percent body fat in a month!" she beamed. (BTW—she was *already* insanely fit before she started training.)

"I'm glad I'm not competing against you." She shrugged her shoulders. I opened my mouth to apologize/explain but she stopped me.

"You don't have to explain a thing to me," and she hugged me.

"I'm going to see you this weekend to cheer you on. Were you practicing in there?" (She was in the Group X room with another competitor.)

"Yeah. It's so weird doing all the poses. You have to remember to do so many things!"

"And the heels you were both wearing are so big!"

"Five inches!"

"You both had the same shoes."

"You have to get clear shoes called Ellies. They elongate your leg."

"Where did you buy them?"

"*Le Rogue*," she whispers.

"What's that?" I ask stupidly.

"It's where all the strippers go to get their heels."

"Oh . . . OH."

We both giggle and chitchat some more. I'm glad she's not mad at me.

Hi! I'm Your Boss! (Part I)

I'm used to being the boss. My guess is that 99.9% of all mothers are THE BOSS at home, because we're better at playing the bad cop than our spouses. I've held various management positions since I was 23 years old and have owned my own company for the past four years. I like being the boss because I am a Type-A personality. Type-A personality means give me a cup of coffee and a deadline and I'm your gal. I am also a control freak. I never volunteer to help out on a committee; I become the committee's chairperson because I like having the control that comes with being the boss.

Anyone who manages people will from time to time have to deal with employees who need a little motivation. In most cases this can be handled fairly quickly and painlessly with a polite but firm chat. Other employees just don't get it and they receive a speech known as, "Hi! I'm Your Boss." Perhaps you've heard it or said it yourself. It is done with more finesse and tact and may not need to cover all the points below, but here is a quick summary of how the speech goes:

You seem to be confused about the nature of our relationship. Allow me to clarify: Hi! I'm Your Boss. I know you want to come to work whenever the hell you want, take a two-hour lunch, go home early and goof off all day, but that's not going to work for me, so you're going to knock your shit off RIGHT NOW. You don't make the rules here; I do. You know why? Because I'm your boss.

Your start time is at 8 o'clock. Not 8:15, not 8:07, not 8:01. It's at 8. What's that? You want to know where I was until 9:30 this morning? Oh, sure. I was at a place called, 'It's none of your f***ing business where I was.' Do you know why? Because I'm *your* boss, you're not *my* boss; I don't report to you.

Speaking of reports, the report is due on the 1st of the month. Not on the 5th, like when you like to hand it in. Do you know why it's due on the 1st and not the 5th? *Because I'm your damn boss and it's due when I say it is.* The 1st of the month is on the 1st of the month. Every month. See that "1" on the calendar? That's when it is. I could give you my calendar if that will help you remember when your deadline is.

What's that? You have a good excuse, I mean reason, why you hand in the report late every month? Uh huh. Oh! OK. Would you like a side order of fries with that bulls**t? You're too busy? Poor baby. I wouldn't know anything about being busy. You are the only person in the entire world who has kids/a pet/a spouse/parents/bills to pay/grocery shopping to do/general and assorted other responsibilities. But guess what? You're going to figure out a way to get me that report on time. You know why? 'Cause I'm your boss.

What's that? It would be easier for you if the report is done this other way? That's nice; the report is to be done the way I want it done. I would love to explain to you why the report needs to be done this particular way and how it all ties in with this other year-end report but if you can't handle a concept as simple and as basic as 'I'm your boss' then I'm really not going to waste my breath explaining my business rationale to you.

I can see by the daggers in your eyes you are throwing at me that you (a) are actually listening to me for once, and (b) don't like me. Guess what? I'm totally cool with you not liking me. Know why? 'Cause I'm not your friend; I'm your boss.

Well, this has been a real fun conversation. You can go back to your cubicle now and sulk like a spanked child for a few minutes, and then I expect you to do your job in the exact prescribed manner we just discussed.

Please leave my office door open, because even though I have a billion other things to do, right now I'm going to watch you to make sure that you are doing your job. Because that's my job. Because I'm your boss.

WEIGH-IN #4—PANIC ATTACK

It was weigh-in/measurement day and I was already in a panic. Everyone in the gym who was training for the Texas Shredder in a week looked amazing; I realized that I still had a long way to go before looking as fit as they did.

Since the last weigh-in, I had lost another 10 pounds, plus two inches in my waist, and my body fat had decreased another 5%. You would think this would make me happy, but I was focused on how much more work needed to be done.

"I have to lose ten percent more body fat before the competition! Oh my God, Daniel, I'm *never* going to be able to do that!"

"Stop freaking out. I'll tweak a few things. I think we're going to have to cut your cardio down to three days a week for a time."

I rolled my eyes and exhaled loudly in disapproval.

"Did you just roll your eyes at me?!"

Oh shit! Now he's going to go all Fifty Shades *on me and make me do 800 lunges or something.*

"When you roll your eyes like that it makes me think that you don't trust me. You have to trust me. I know what I'm doing." (*Unlike you*, he implied.)

Here's what I thought:

It's not that I don't trust you, it's that, **OK—I DON'T TRUST YOU!!!** I don't trust *myself.* I've never been as in shape as these women getting ready to go onstage, even when I was 107 pounds and starving. I've yo-yo dieted for the past two decades and nothing ever lasts longer than a week. I get to the weight I want and then it seems like I drink an extra glass of water and gain it all back plus seven more. I'm not getting any younger, my metabolism is slowing down, and **I'LL NEVER, NEVER, NEVER LOOK LIKE THOSE BIKINI CHICKS ONSTAGE!!! Why are you so blasé about this?!?**

Here's what I muttered: "I trust you."

He wasn't buying what I was selling and shook his head in annoyed exasperation with me. "Look how far you've come since you've been training with me! You lost almost twenty-five pounds! You went from twenty-nine percent body fat to twenty-one percent body fat in two months! You're eleven weeks out from your show. Of course you're going to be ready for this competition!"

(Note to self: Do not question Daniel's authority as a trainer. This just pisses him off.)

"Well, should I cut the calories on my diet?" I sulked.

"No. I want you to follow the plan I gave you. It's not your job to worry about how to reach your fitness goals; that's my job. Just follow the plan **EXACTLY** as I gave it to you."

HI! I'M YOUR BOSS! (PART II)!

My "Hi! I'm Your Boss" speech, which is never fun to give, is even worse to receive. I know this because I am now in the unfamiliar and uncomfortable position of having my trainer, Daniel, as my boss of sorts. True, I hired him to be my trainer, but that entails me doing what he tells me to do . . . which kinda sucks.

While I don't know the inner workings of his mind, here is what I think his inside voice wants to say to all his pain-in-the-ass clients (myself included) (aka "Normal People"):

You seem to be confused about the nature of our relationship. Allow me to clarify. Hi! I'm Your Trainer. I know you want to eat whatever the hell you want, read a romance novel instead of run on the treadmill, and still miraculously lose weight, but that's not happening on Planet Reality, so you're going to knock your shit off RIGHT. NOW. You don't make the rules at the gym; I do. You know why? Because I'm your trainer.

If I say do 30 minutes of cardio before we meet, that's 30 minutes. Not 25, not 23-ish. It's 30 minutes. What's that? You want to know why you have to listen to me? Because you hired me to train you! I didn't seek you out at the grocery store; you sought me out. To be your trainer . . . So stop fighting me and let me train you!

Speaking of training, how long will it take for you to train yourself to keep up the food journal daily? Not every other week, like when you like to update it. Daily. Do you know why it should be updated daily and not weekly? Because I'm your damn trainer and it's due when I say it is. Seriously, it takes like two seconds, especially if you are following the meal plan I gave you.

What's that? Ohhhhh. You're NOT following the meal plan I gave you, which is why you're not logging in your food journal because you think you're pulling a fast one on me. OK, first, you're not pulling anything over on me because I get paid if you gain 8 pounds or lose 30, so you're only fooling yourself here.

Second, when I say "meal plan," what I really mean is "you better plan on following that diet I just gave you," because when you don't follow it we both know what happens. But you don't have to take my opinion, just consult your size 14 jeans.

Just follow your diet and do the very simple exercise routine I showed you how to do. I even gave you a calendar outlining which muscle groups to work on each day. What's that? You have a good excuse, I mean "reason," why you couldn't work out? Uh huh. Oh! OK. Would you like a side order of fries with that bullshit?

You're too busy? Poor baby. I wouldn't know anything about being busy or dealing with a girlfriend who complains I don't have any time for her because all I ever do is work or work out. No, no, YOU are the only person in the entire world who has kids/a pet/a spouse/parents/bills to pay/grocery shopping to do/general and assorted other responsibilities. But guess what? You're going to figure out a way to get into the gym. You know why? 'Cause I'm your trainer and I will bug the living shit out of you if you don't. What's that? It's hard for you to not have a beer with your friends on St. Patrick's Day? Try saying no to beer when your roommate decides to throw a party in your own apartment three weeks before your bodybuilding competition. I had to drink 3 gallons of ice water with lemon slices while everyone else got trashed and had a good time. You don't hear me crying to you about it, do you?

What's that? It would be easier for you to do weights in the morning and cardio in the afternoon? That's nice; the exercise routine is to be done the way I said to do it. Comprende? I would love to explain to you why cardio needs to be done on an empty stomach and weight training is done on a full stomach, but if you can't handle a concept as simple and as basic as 'I'm your trainer' then I'm really not going to waste my breath explaining my metabolism rationale to you.

I see by the daggers in your eyes you are throwing at me that you (a) are actually listening to me for once, and (b) don't like me. Guess what? I'm totally cool with you not liking me. Know why? 'Cause I'm not your friend; I'm your trainer.

Please know that you can't hide from me in the gym, because I live here; I sleep on the treadmill and my pillow is a 50 lb. weight. Also, in case you haven't noticed, there are mirrors everywhere, so I totally see you from all angles when you show up late or when your form is wrong. And I will call you out on it.

Well, this has been a real fun conversation. You can go back to the elliptical machine now and sulk like a spanked child for a few minutes, and then I expect you to follow your meal plan and exercise calendar in the exact prescribed manner we just discussed. And you WILL stretch. You know why? BECAUSE I'm your damn trainer and I SAID SO!

Even though I have a billion other things to do, right now I'm going to watch you to make sure that you do what you are supposed to do. Because that's what I'm supposed to do. Because I'm your trainer.

So I guess I'll just shut the hell up now and do what I'm told, 'cause even though I'm the boss in the workplace, looks like he's the boss in the gym. Damn it.

MENTAL STRENGTH: YOU DON'T HAVE IT

The snooze button can't be pressed fast enough on my cell phone. My 2-year-old son is upside down in the bed and his legs are resting across my head. I don't even remember him coming in. Henri is snoring. I force myself to wake and get out of bed. It's 5:20 a.m.

I'm supposed to do 30 minutes of cardio before we meet for our 6:00 a.m. session. *Yeah, good luck with that,* I think sleepily as I weigh myself, dress and drink some creatine powder mixed with orange juice.

Driving along the quiet streets I curse the red traffic lights. *No one's on the road but crazy gym rats like me; can't you just be green?* I get a new diet today . . .

I punch in my code, grab a towel from the front desk and head back to the locker room to deposit my backpack. I get on the stationary bike and begin to pedal. It's 5:42 a.m. I don't see Daniel anywhere. *Good.*

CNN is on and the panel is discussing the primary. I stand up and pedal faster. I'm supposed to keep my heart rate up. I drink my BCAA water and get a burst of energy. I'm feeling warm now, but not sweaty, and notice Daniel is at the check-in area.

We exchange pleasantries and get into the new diet. I'm excited to switch things up. I really want to lose the last 10 pounds currently residing around my midsection. I'm pretty sure the banana nut muffin I ate two days ago is not helping with that, but in my defense, it's not like I actively sought it out. Our neighbor brought it over, freshly baked from her oven. I couldn't be rude, could I? Especially since it smelled so very good and was still warm.

I haven't updated my food journal yet because I know he's going on vacation to prepare for his competition, and I will update the log when he is gone in an attempt to bury the evidence with other food entries. Pretty clever, huh?

"How's the diet going?"

"Well, it's been a little rough the past few weeks, after the flu & cheater's weekend and all." This is a partial truth. The flu did mess with my appetite. The muffin just messed with my waistline.

He shakes his head at me. "You need to log in your food every day. It takes five minutes."

"I've been busy with -"

"I don't care. No excuses."

Grr.

"We're not going to do weigh-in or measurements until after I get back because of your recent bout with the flu and I don't want you to stress out and obsess over your lack of weight loss."

Relief washes over me. He'll never know about the muffin. "Oh good, you know me," I say happily.

Yes . . . yes he does . . .

"Did you warm up for thirty minutes today?"

"Yeah—" I caught his eyebrow arch so I switched my lie to a half-truth mid-sentence. "For like twenty-five-ish minutes."

"Twenty-five minutes, huh?"

"Maybe twenty-three-ish?"

"Because I was here on the treadmill at five a.m. and when I finished at five thirty you weren't here."

Busted. Again. Damn.

"You're eleven weeks out, Lisa. If I say you need to do thirty minutes of cardio before weights that means thirty minutes. Not twenty-three-ish. Get up earlier."

It's going to be one of *those* mornings . . .

We walk to the incline press. Today is chest/shoulders day. I hate chest/shoulders days because this is my weakest muscle group. I'm kinda hating Daniel too 'cause he just called me out for two things already and we haven't even picked up a dumbbell yet. He puts the weights on the bar and I'm just pressing away, fueled with righteous indignation. *Why is he so tough on me? Why am I even doing this stupid competition? I hate you, Daniel.*

"See that lady in the black shirt? She's competing next week. Do you think she's ready?"

I look at the Asian woman. Her arms are toned but her stomach is still flabby. Don't get me wrong—by no means was she out of shape, but she did not look like she was ready for a panel of judges to compare her body against others.

"Oh, she's not ready at all," I say sympathetically.

"No. She's not. She has lots of excuses, though. And there is another woman who started training the same time as her. They were the same weight, same height, same body fat. But the other woman is ten pounds lighter, has more muscle definition, and is ready for the competition and this lady is not."

I feel my stomach tighten and it's not from isometrics. I complete the next two sets quietly and we move to the free weights.

"I'll bet the other lady doesn't have kids," I say lifting the dumbbells.

"She has four, actually. Two are older and two are younger. She coordinates with their father so she can train." *I walked into that trap. I'm sure he knew I was going to ask if she had kids.*

"Don't take this the wrong way, Lisa, but the other lady has the **mental strength** to really focus on her diet and eat clean."

Unlike me, he not so subtly implied.

Is there a right way to take that?

I drive home feeling incredibly frustrated and embarrassed. Training with Daniel is nothing like I expected it to be. I thought he would show me how to lift weights and tell me to eat salad with low-cal dressing, not call me out constantly on my bullshit and constantly imply that my best isn't good enough. I've never been pushed so hard mentally and physically and my emotions are still raw from the sting of last November, when my world was untangling. I can't help but think of my meltdown, the breaking point that led me to bodybuilding in the first place.

MELTDOWN—LAST NOVEMBER

My father died a long time ago but it seems to me sometimes that I was only just speaking with him yesterday. The 10th anniversary of his death is approaching and for whatever reason it's just been hitting me hard, and I'm not sure why.

Well, that's not entirely true. I miss him more right now because I'm lost and feel very much alone.

The family "favorite" fell in a traditional manner in my house. My brother is my mom's favorite and I was Daddy's girl. When you're a Daddy's girl you learn what unconditional love truly means. My mother—oh sure, she loves me, but in Daddy's eyes I could do no wrong. And if I did do wrong, he was sure that it was due to some outside source and not my own flawed character.

When you're Daddy's girl it means you're the prettiest one in the room, even though you wear glasses and have braces, a bad haircut and acne. Because when he looks at you he sees how far you've come from the past, overlooks the present circumstances, and is excited for your future.

Marriage is different; love of a husband is conditional. If you don't believe this, talk to the 50% of the population who is divorced. I didn't feel relevant. I'd given up my career. My kids would start school next fall and their friends would become a louder voice than mine in no time. My mother had my brother. My husband had his job. I had no one to hold onto anymore; everyone important to me was leaving me, so I found myself missing my father more.

I missed having someone look past my weight gain and money woes, my bad haircut and wrinkling skin. I longed to have someone look at me and:

See the strengths of my past,
Overlook the mess of my current circumstances, and
Believe that I still had a bright future.

My husband is very fit, through no effort of his own. He was blessed with a fantastic metabolism. He gets McDonald's for breakfast, doesn't eat lunch, eats whatever for dinner—usually a Marie Callender's frozen dinner—and after the kids go to bed, we self-medicate with rum and Coke and chips and dip in front of the TV. And he never gains weight. EVER.

I went from a size 3 when we met to a size 14 at my worst. I've tried every diet known to womankind and they all work for awhile, until I stop. Maybe Henri is right; I lack self-control. Or maybe I've just put it on mute for about half a decade. In fairness to my lackadaisical approach to dieting, there is no real reward for becoming thin. The "cleanse" works incredibly well if you can keep it going for 10 days in a row. I went all the way down to size 5 in 10 days (no shit, really—pardon the pun), and my husband still wouldn't touch me. It was then that it was painfully confirmed that his lack of desire had nothing to do with my weight, so long used as an excuse for his indifference toward me, but the simple truth was that he wanted nothing to do with me at all.

After 11 years of being together, seven years married—almost five with kids—it made me sad to think our relationship was unraveling. We built a business together; we built a family together; we built a home together, but suddenly I felt desperately alone.

You can build up a lot of resentments in 11 years. I used to be an actress. He sort of thought it was cool, but mostly didn't understand what I did or why I was so passionate about something that made me no money. I quit on my dream for various reasons, but a piece of me blames him. It's not fair to him, really. In all honesty my "career" wasn't going so well so when he suggested I take a break from it for awhile he had given me an easy out and thus also became a scapegoat for why I quit. But after defining myself as an artist for so long it really put me in a tailspin when I had to figure out what to do next.

I was 107 pounds when I met him. It still wasn't thin enough for him. He stood me in front of a mirror. I was wearing matching bra and panties— purple silk with a blue line coming across them—and he traced the outside of my thighs.

"If you could just tighten up here and here your body would be rockin'!"

Alas, that was as rocked as my body ever was. I had been living with my boyfriend in NY and after we split up I dropped 15 pounds and moved to L.A. That's when I met Henri. And now two kids and almost 50 pounds later, yeah, there were a lot of resentments between us.

He blamed me for moving to Texas. He loved California but there was no way we could afford the lifestyle we wanted plus let me be a stay-at-home-mom there. Texas allowed us to live champagne dreams on a beer budget.

He was in sales. I didn't like him doing that. He was always in bars networking, coming home at all hours, if not drunk then certainly buzzed beyond the point of driving safely. I worried about him getting a DUI. I worried about him cheating on me. If we could just get away from the wheeling and dealing world of Cali we would be a closer family, I thought.

So we cashed out of our jobs, packed up our kids (we moved two months after the second baby was born), and headed into Texas. We bought a 27-unit apartment building that we thought would earn us tons of cash. We were pretty f***ing stupid to think that. The Great Recession hit, our credit became a block of ice, and Henri had to take over running the day-to-day maintenance of the run-down piece of shit we just purchased.

He traded in high-end clothing for ripped construction jeans and his cell phone for a hammer and went to work renovating our ghetto-fabulous property. In his old job people used to hand him piles of cash and they thanked him for it. Here, our tenants handed us $400 per month and complained about the plumbing. Henri was called for repairs nights, weekends, and holidays and he hated it. He felt like a janitor and he blamed me for it.

In California I was shy. My friendships went only as deep as the monthly reports that we worked on together or the latest Jon Stewart quote over the water cooler. Henri had friends to hang out with morning, noon and night. They were real friends too, and I liked them, but I was always, and would always only be, Henri's wife. I was never Lisa.

Here in Texas he only saw his tenants, who wanted him to fix stuff, or the workers he hired, who wanted a raise. Even though he went out for beers with them from time-to-time everyone felt the social order of things and he could never truly unwind.

I had the complete opposite experience. Once my daughter went to nursery school I had an instant group of mommy friends. We talked about potty training and nursing our newest babies; traded chicken recipes and Morgan's Deal coupons for random things. We were all heavily invested in the cultivation of our children and were able to share the burdens of motherhood together. . As I was ascending, my husband was descending.

He was angry. He was tired. He said things that hurt me in ways that only a married person knows how to do. He had no interest in me. It annoyed him when I would read *Newsweek*. It annoyed him when I would dabble at writing a novel. It annoyed him that I could find time to volunteer to chair a fund-raiser for a nursery school but not find time to clip coupons, as he had asked. It annoyed him that my life seemed more fun than his.

I was size 10 the night of the fund-raiser. I was trying to work for the school in exchange for tuition, but it didn't work out. Henri told me not to volunteer anymore and even though I agreed, I suddenly found myself isolated from everyone outside our family and I had nothing to look forward to but diapers and laundry. That was last May. By November I had to buy size 14 jeans, and even they are feeling tight.

Sometimes it felt like my husband hated me. I think he thought the same thing of me. We both felt the distance between us but didn't know how to fix it.

And I just began to eat. I didn't even taste anything. It wasn't even like I bought cupcakes or anything fun. I just ate whatever was near me. By November I was 150 pounds. People were asking me if I was pregnant.

"No, I'm just fat," I smiled, feeling like shit on the inside. And then, one day, he said it.

"Lisa, I will always love you. I'm just not attracted to you right now."

I'm wandering through my house in a fog. Dishes are piled in the sink, laundry sits on the couch waiting to be folded. My husband's papers cover the dining room table, toys are scattered on the floor. Looking from one corner to the next I see no area that is truly clean; my house is as cluttered as the thoughts in my brain. Why can't I seem to organize anything? I used to be so organized.

Little Man is banging some pots on the floor. I've reheated the same cup of coffee four times and can't seem to remember where I've placed it last. Oh, the dining room table. I hope no one knocks at the door because I'd be embarrassed if they saw this. Bills are stacked, unopened, in a pile. To look at them seems to be admitting defeat. The medical bills, the bills from the business; we can't pay any of them right now.

My mom loaned us the $6,000 for Rylee to go to nursery school, but knows we can't pay her back, so she said it was a gift. Rylee goes half-days because even with the loan, I couldn't afford the full-day tuition. She doesn't understand why she leaves at noon when all her friends stay until 2 p.m. She thinks I'm being mean when I pack her lunch on pizza day, because we just don't have the extra five dollars each week.

Draining my lukewarm coffee, I go into my husband's sock drawer and find $20 and begin to tear up, realizing that I've been reduced to scavenging for money through my husband's things. I used to make six figures. I used to have my own cash. It all went into the business and I have nothing to show for it.

My throat is scratchy and I wipe my nose with the back of my hand because I'm classy like that sometimes. Little Henry doesn't want a new diaper and won't lay down, so I change him standing up, fighting with him to get him into his jeans jacket and struggling to get him locked and loaded in the car. I hand him a sippy cup of milk and drive into Austin.

Fighting back tears, weaving through traffic against a pale gray sky, the buildings look foreboding and I feel completely and utterly alone. Little Man is asleep now, as I pull into the quiet parking lot. Parking along the fence, facing the leaves changing with the colors of autumn, it feels as if the whole world is collapsing around me. If not the whole world, then my world at least.

I wanted to make love but he refused. He tells me he's too tired, too stressed about work, about money. But the simple truth is he doesn't want me anymore.

"Lisa, I will always love you," he said, "I'm just not attracted to you right now."

Children are playing on the playground, giggling and laughing, and I'm gripping my steering wheel and watching the tears drip over my white knuckles, tracing down my fingertips. My wedding ring is too tight, so I haven't worn it in a week or so, but it doesn't really matter because I know what's going to happen next. Husbands always love their first wives, that's why their second wives look like a younger, prettier version of the first one.

I can't live like this anymore. Maybe if I can just get myself together, maybe everything else will get better too. But I don't know how to do that.

Please, God, please fix me. Whatever is wrong with me, just fix me.

OOHRAH MARINE

Driving home from the gym, I physically shake my head because I'm shaking away last year's autumn memories from my mind. I'm shaking away Daniel's reprimands too. Walking into my house, I'm in a fog again, only this time it's different. Because it's five months later and Henri is helping with the kids now. The house is not a mess now. The bills are getting paid now.

"You look so pretty today," Henri says kissing me on his way out the door.

I'm lying in my bed now, napping with my son, as Rylee plays with her puzzle on the floor. All sorts of thoughts are rolling through my brain as I drift in and out of sleep. "We don't have the money for this," "No excuses," "Why can't you work out later, Mommy?" "You don't have the mental strength to do this." I'm thinking of my weight, the competition, my high school reunion, my wedding anniversary, the 10th anniversary of my father's passing.

I was dreaming about my father's funeral. The sound from the rifle echoes in my ears. Then I realize Rylee is at my side wanting some orange juice.

"In a minute, OK?" I pull her into bed with me to cuddle. "I can't believe you're turning five soon." I hug my children close as they nod off, and tears roll down my face. I wonder where the time went. I wonder, chuckling, what my dad would think about me entering a bikini contest.

My father was an enlisted man; he was in the Air Force. Like many immigrant sons, not only did he see the military as a chance to escape a life doomed to working in the local factory, but he was proud to be American. His parents came from Sweden through Ellis Island in the early part of the century not knowing the language or a soul beyond the relative who sponsored them. My grandma became a janitor for the school. My grandpa worked construction. My dad wanted more.

His timing was impeccable. He enlisted after Korea but before Vietnam, and when he entered the workforce he had some college credits under his belt and became a computer programmer in the ' 60s.

He died May 24, 2002. It was Memorial Day weekend. Soldiers in crisp uniforms played taps, fired their guns, and folded a flag and gave it to my mother. The sky was as pale blue as my father's eyes.

Before he died I signed up for my first race, a 5k where the proceeds went to cancer research; I gave him my race bib. "I'm running for you," I said. After he died in 2002, I ran marathons in his honor, four in all. I ran with Team In Training. You promise to raise money for cancer research and they train you to complete an endurance sport of your choice.

My second marathon was the Marine Corps Marathon in Washington, D.C. It was 2005, the height of the War in Iraq. For that one I held a casino night fund-raiser that raised about $25,000. This was the marathon for which I trained the hardest. I was also a team mentor to help other people finish their race and complete their fundraising goals. My husband, mom and brother were able to attend a dinner where it was announced I was the #3 fund-raiser in the country. Mom whispered, "Dad would have been so proud."

A marathon is 26.2 miles. In ancient Greece, Phidippides, a professional runner, was tasked by a Greek general to run from Marathon to Athens to warn the Athenians that the Persians were coming to attack. Phidippides made the 26-mile trek in about three hours and then promptly died. (He had previously run 140 miles each way to Sparta to ask for military backup, fought a battle in heavy armor all day and then was asked to run to Athens. And you thought *your* boss was a task master!) It is for this reason you will see marathon runners sometimes wear shirts that say, "Why couldn't Phidippides die at mile 20?"

The extra .2 miles was added to the official marathon length in 1908 during the Olympics in London so the finish line could end in front of King Edward VII's royal box. This is why some people call out, "God save the Queen!" at mile 26. But most people at mile 26 are just trying to make it to the finish line.

Even though I trained with the team I decided to run my own race and not stay with a running partner. I had run up Torrey Pines Hill every Monday night to increase my endurance and speed and lifted light weights in the gym to increase my strength. Until recently, this was the most powerful I ever felt physically. I think I weighed about 125 pounds.

But at mile 17 (damn that mile 17) I was fading fast. I had run over the Potomac, through a forest, and past the Washington Monument. The end was at the Lincoln Monument. My knee was bound tightly in medical tape so my patella wouldn't move but the strain was beginning to come. The pain was sharp.

I was running alone with no one to divert my attention and I wore no iPod for safety reasons. I thought I was going to die. Slowing my pace I saw people I knew pass me. Everyone wears a timer chip in their shoelaces and loved ones can follow your progress online or via text. I had been at a good pace, but suddenly I had slowed. Henri sent me a text. "R u OK?"

Marines were running past me. People running for cancer were running past me. Everyone's shirts were decorated with bubble paint. Mine had my name, "Lisa," on it and "4 Dad" on it too. I read the shirts around me. "In memory of Mom," "In honor of Jack." Fallen heroes listed on each runner's back. A man was running with a streamer of names of soldiers who had died in Iraq. The emotions are overwhelming when you see pictures of children who are sick and yellow ribbons begging for husbands to come home.

No one could do anything for these lost people, but we could run and we could remember them. But I was ready to stop. I swallowed some GU, which is like a very sweet jelly designed to give you instant energy. I felt nothing. I poured water on my head. It didn't help.

An African American marine was standing at the top of the hill and he was looking at me, watching me falter and fail. He called out to me, "I see you, Lisa!"

I looked up at him.

"That's right, I see you. I'm calling out to you because I know you can do this. And I see you're doing this for your father. And he knows you can do this too!"

Suddenly I was soaring. My face exploded into a smile.

"Oohrah," I mouthed as I passed the marine on the hill, never stopping to look back until I had crossed that finish line.

Daniel's words roll through my brain like a freight train. With each passing moment the anger rises inside me. *Mental strength . . . I don't have the mental strength?!* I ran *four* marathons. This is not something a weak-willed person can do.

I climbed the corporate ladder to senior management; started my own business with my husband; self-published a book that won a Mom's Choice Award. Does he have any idea how much courage it takes to gamble on yourself like that?

My breath is getting ragged with rage. I helped my mom care for my father as he lay dying of cancer, never shedding a tear in front of him. I'm raising two kids and I'm fighting to fix my marriage. And you think I don't have the *mental strength* to compete in a *bikini contest?*

Kid, you don't know a damn thing about me and my mental strength.

So even though I want to stay in bed and stress about the weeks ahead or cry about the days behind, I know I can do this and get focused on the moment before me. I'm tired of this pity party I've been throwing myself. I get out of bed. It's time to get in the game because I have a bright future ahead of me.

The next morning I am up at 4 a.m. Before he even shows up I do the full 50-minute cardio workout on my exercise calendar plus the 10 minutes of stretching in the sauna he added on this week. I drank the protein powder from the diet.

He enters the check-in area. I hand him a small silver gift bag with stars on it.

"What's this?" he asks surprised. He is smiling, confused.

"Good luck at your competition. Read the card first." It says to use the gift with annoying clients full of excuses. He opens the bag and pulls out a red button with the word BULLSHIT on it that flashes red and says, "Warning! This is complete bullshit!" He laughs.

"Guess the pep talk worked?"

Pep talk. Oh, that's what he calls it.

After eight weeks of telling him nothing but half-truths, excuses, rationalizations and outright lies (every single one of them which he promptly exposed and called me out on), I was tired of listening to my own bullshit. I decided it was time to just be honest with him and, more importantly, myself, and train to win.

Because, of course, I have the mental strength to do this.

"Lisa, you just made my day."

I CAN'T BELIEVE YOU WON'T LET ME EAT I CAN'T BELIEVE IT'S NOT BUTTER

It's our last session before Daniel's vacation/The Texas Shredder. I'm super excited because he gives me my new ~~diet~~ (sorry) "meal plan" today. I love getting a new diet every two weeks. But wait . . . this can't be right . . .

"I can eat butter?!" My hand is over my mouth to contain my amazement.

"No; you can eat I Can't Believe It's Not Butter. It's a butter substitute with zero calories."

I continue looking through my meal plan. I can drink coffee now. And. And. And . . . DIET COKE?

"I can drink Diet Coke too? Oh my God, Daniel, you made my week!"

Oh shit. He's got that look. Like he's about to call me out for something and I didn't even do anything yet.

"Lisa, when you make statements like, 'You just made my week,' it makes me think you're going to go overboard."

"I won't go overboard."

Three days later . . .

Daniel: U WENT OVERBOARD!

Uh oh. The texts are still coming. My cell phone is practically dancing from the four or five incoming texts buzzing in succession now. I don't want to read them.

Daniel: IT'S THE BUTTER SPRAY! NOT THE TUB!

Lisa: I thought I was doing something wrong.

Daniel: 2,200 CALORIES!?!

I knew that stupid online food journal would get me in trouble again! I thought he was off this week; why is he checking it? What kind of a person works on his week off?

Lisa: Yeah, but I figured that out, and now I'm back down to 1,550 calories.

See how calm and rational I am? Plus I self-corrected my dieting error and bought the spray on my own after reading the calorie count. Yay me!

Daniel: U r not drinking enough water!

Lisa: Well, u said I could have Diet Coke . . .

Daniel: ONE Diet Coke! Not 4! NO MORE I CAN'T BELIEVE IT'S NOT BUTTER! NO MORE DIET COKES!

All caps? Really?

Lisa: OK.

He's real crabby because his competition is tomorrow and he's eating nothing but egg whites and distilled water. But still . . . I can't believe he won't let me eat I Can't Believe It's Not Butter.

GARAGE SALE

"Your pants are falling off you," Daniel said the other day.

I had finished dressing in the locker room and was walking toward the exit. Daniel was standing by the front desk waiting for his next client and counting down the minutes till his vacation, I'm sure. I was wearing a black T-shirt and my size 5 khakis, but even with a belt they were falling off my hips.

"Yeah, I know," I smiled awkwardly.

"Good excuse to go shopping, right?"

"Uh huh. Have a nice vacation."

I scurried out.

Remember how I told you that prior to starting this whole bikini project I refused to buy anymore big girl clothes, so I had like two pairs of jeans that fit, and I was wearing a handful of my husband's T-shirts because everything in my closet was too small for me to cram myself into? Well, now I have an entirely new dilemma: Now everything in my closet is too big for me.

Don't get me wrong—this is the most fantastic predicament I've ever had. I'm down to size 4. The last time I saw size 4 was during my Buffy days, when I weighed 107 pounds. The year was 1999 and everyone wore baby doll T's exposing their cute little midriffs just like Britney Spears. *Please note*: Once you have given birth, all crop tops should be burned. When you are in the hospital they should just make it an even exchange: they give you a baby, and you give them all your baby doll T's.

My size 3 jeans back from My Buffy Weight days were given to Goodwill years ago. I have some size 4 business suits still, like what I wore Easter Sunday, but that's hardly appropriate attire for going to Story Time at the library. Even my belts are too big on me now.

If we were doing well financially, I'd just go shopping, but every dollar counts, so I casually test the waters with Henri.

"I need to buy some new clothes."

"Shop in your closet," he says.

"Nothing in there fits anymore, Henri."

And of course the unspoken elephant in the room is, *What if I gain all the weight back?* How much am I going to spend on a new wardrobe that will only fit me for a month? I know that I'm definitely getting rid of all the size 14s and 12s because I hate them, and I feel like I know enough now about food to never allow myself to get back there. But what about my size 8s? Size 8 is like my own personal line of demarcation. Once I cross it, I'm right into 10s and 12s three weeks later.

In a stroke of brilliance, I decide I'll have a garage sale and use the money I make to buy some new clothes! Not so brilliantly, the garage sale is the same morning as the Shredder, because I don't always think things through before posting signs around the neighborhood.

I have a wide variety of children's toys, clothes, strollers and then my own stuff. I get rid of all my large shirts, plus pants ranging from size 9 to14. I couldn't let go of the 8s, but just this much is therapeutic.

The kids keep coming outside wanting to play with their toys I'm pawning, and while the door is open a bird flies inside our house. Big Henri is busy discussing the merits of a stuffed Cookie Monster with a Mexican woman, and I'm looking at the time on my phone. I should be leaving for the show in about 15 minutes.

So, should I tell Henri about the bird in the house, knowing he will want me to spend the next hour helping him hunt it down, or should I say nothing and let him organically discover the bird on his own?

Guess what I did?

Fifteen minutes later and $45 richer, all the customers were gone and Big Henri was picking up the leftovers. I bent down to pick up a toy, and when I stood up, my pants fell down around my ankles. I have two things to say about this:

- Sorry about that wardrobe malfunction, neighbors!
- At least I was wearing the Victoria Secret undies.

Henri had one thing to say about this: "You need to go shopping." (And nice undies, hon.)

Yes!

We went inside where Henri was able to put an extra hole in my belt, ensuring that I wouldn't have to worry about flashing people at the competition. And with that, I was off to the Shredder!

TEXAS SHREDDER

The Texas Shredder is held at a local high school gym. The day is divided into two sections: prejudging, which takes place in the morning, and the actual show, which starts at 6 p.m. and where the awards are given out. I attend the prejudging, because it is (a) only $10 vs. $25 for the night show, and (b) I'm really interested to see what this whole bodybuilding thing is about, and what makes a person win.

The place is mobbed, and I am sitting in the top bleachers. The first thing that hits you is an overwhelming scent of spray tan. The crowd is a mixture of bodybuilder types and "normal" people. The bodybuilder peeps wear shirts that say things like "House of Pain," "Eat Clean/Train Dirty," and "Moms Kick Butt." (I bought the Moms Kick Butt shirt. That leaves me $20 to buy a new wardrobe at Walmart.)

There is also a vendor table set up with racks and racks of posing suits. I look at the price tag—$350??? Some are even $600! Oh my God, my husband is going to have a heart attack when he finds out how much I have to pay.

"Looking for something particular?" the nice woman asks.

"I'm going to do my first show, the bikini division for old people, but not until June. I still have a lot of weight to lose, so I'll just buy it after Memorial Day, when I'm thinner."

"Honey, if this is your first show, you better get your suit early so you can practice posing."

"Oh, I didn't think of that."

There's actually a lot I have to think about. I have to get a posing suit. I have to get the required high heels. I have to figure out how to stand onstage in said bikini and heels without falling over. Everything is suddenly starting to seem real to me. Oh my God, I'm going to be standing onstage 10 weeks from now and I'm utterly unready.

Why did I eat that muffin the other day? Why did I bring M&M's in the house? Was I nuts?

There is an NPC table set up too. NPC stands for National Physique Committee, and it is one of the governing bodies of the amateur bodybuilding competitions. You have to purchase your NPC card for $100 before you can sign up to do a competition. The competition, by the way, is another fee— $85 per category you decide to compete in. For example, I can compete in the Bikini division, which is open to all women, or just the Bikini Masters division, which is only for women ages 35 and older, and/or I could do both, but that's a lot of money.

There is a pretty blonde woman sitting behind the table.

"I would like to buy an NPC card, please."

"Which division? Figure?"

"I would like the bikini division for senior citizens."

"What?" She laughs. "It's called Masters division. That sounds a lot better."

I pay with a credit card. This is actually pretty exciting! I sign the card and smile. I can't believe I'm doing this. I'm going to be in a bikini competition! Me!

I find an empty seat in the auditorium, all the way in the back. There are different groups onstage and I'm trying to understand what's going on. The women are led onstage in groups of 15 it seems, but there must be over 40 of them on the stage. The man leading them is big, bald, and bored. The women look like they just drank six Red Bulls before coming onstage. High energy and nerves aside, they look fantastic. I mean *really fantastic*. These women are not thin; they are *ripped* and still completely feminine. I can't help but think that each person's body represents at least $2,000 of supplements, training, gym memberships, bikinis, heels, spray tans, sparkly earrings, blood, sweat, and tears.

Henri sends me a text.

Henri: How's it going?
Lisa: Interesting. I didn't know there would be so many people.

I take a picture and send him a picture of the crowd. He sends me his own picture. It's of a bird that's in our top windowsill in the family room.

Henri: Do you know how a bird got in our house?
Lisa: A bird? Whoa! Crazy. TTYL.

The first group of women do four poses: front stance, side stance, other side, then back. I see my friend from the gym, Obidia, onstage! She looks beautiful! I've only ever seen her with a ponytail, but today her hair was down and curled, and she was wearing make-up. The women all pull their hair over one shoulder and stick their butts out and hold their chests up. Their bikinis glitter in the lights and a crisscross connects the top and bottom portion of their suits. Everyone wears a number on her left hip and after the initial poses the handler makes them stand in a V. Then judges call out five numbers and the women stand on Xs on the stage. The judges make them switch places and remove one person and call in another. Photographers snap photos. Women leave the stage.

Now the men enter. What a contrast! Whereas the women were lean and packed onstage like sardines, the men seemed HUGE! Five bodies filled the entire stage, but there were two rows of men crammed in there. And . . . is that Daniel? I think it is. It's hard to tell because (a) I'm sitting in the nosebleed section of the bleachers, (b) everyone is spray tanned and looks like they've joined a new ethnicity and, (c) I've only ever seen Daniel in knee length gym shorts and a red 24 Hour Fitness shirt, and all the men here are in very small posing suits and are pretty close to being naked.

A crowd of people in the front part of the auditorium shout, "Daniel!" so I'm assuming that must be his family. One competitor seems to have had an issue with the tanning spray: he's bright red instead of tan, and looks like his skin was peeled back to expose his muscles. Another is pasty white, and you can't see any muscle definition whatsoever.

The men do their individual poses. Daniel looks nervous, but his family shouts again and he laughs and his poses look a lot better when he is at ease. Then they do the call outs, five at a time. The first man stands in the middle and then they call Daniel's number! He's being considered for 2nd place! They call out the other three men to make the top five group, and have them to do a front pose where their arms are lifted above their chest. Well, 1st place guy gets into Daniel's space, so Daniel takes his arm and puts it in front of the other guy. *Oh snap!* Can you smell the testosterone?

The judges say, "Guys, give each other space." They are told to do another pose. *Oh no he didn't!* First place guy gets in Daniel's space again! Now Daniel moves his arm in front. Then the other guy moves *his* arm in front, and now I'm getting really interested because for an instant it seems like this is going to become bodybuilding boxing. How cool would that be?

But the judge tells the 1st place guy to go back on his mark. Then, when they are told to leave the stage, the rude guy pats Daniel on his shoulder and says something laughing, and Daniel laughs too. Wait . . . they were just about to get in a fight, but now they're laughing? I have no idea what just transpired. Maybe it's just a guy thing? I will never understand men.

I've been texting pictures of everyone onstage to my husband, who used to be a bodybuilder in his 20s.

Henri: Only a few look like they are on steroids.

Lisa: Oh, no, Henri, everyone is drug tested.

Henri: My sweet, naive wife, there are ways to cheat a drug test.

Hmm.

Two women next to me are talking about just that: Some supplement to take to kick up your workouts. But then the bikini women enter the stage and the whole crowd becomes alert. These women have spunk. The figure women were structured, and their poses were very crisp. Not the bikini babes. They were all about sassy swagger. They stuck their booties out, lifted their breasts up and rocked those bikinis.

OMG, how am I ever going to do that?

Before the competition Daniel told me not to get intimidated by the other women. In his Jedi Master way the message rang loud and clear: Be afraid. Be very afraid.

After the prejudging I sent Daniel a text.

Lisa: U were great!

Daniel: Thx!

Lisa: That guy next to u was a jerk!

Daniel: LOL. Nah, he was my competitor.

Daniel: What do you think about bodybuilding?

Lisa: It's fascinating. And I will never cheat on my diet again.
Daniel: Good!

STRIKE A POSE/SASSY LESSONS

I arrive Monday morning at the gym and Daniel is beaming. He won 2nd place in his division at the Texas Shredder Classic. "Well, you earned it," I tell him.

Today he's going to teach me how to do the four female poses for the competition. We go into the Group X room where there are a ton of mirrors, and I roll up my shirt so my stomach is showing. I'm wearing my new "Moms Kick Butt" tank top. I love it.

"There are four poses for the female competition. Front, right side, back, and left side. For males, the important thing is to look as big as possible. For females, the important thing is to be sassy."

Well, now I get the giggles, because I don't know what's funnier to me: having this big bulky guy trying to teach me how to stand like a woman, or hearing him use a word like *sassy*.

The back pose is the hardest for me because you're supposed to engage your lat muscles while keeping your arms relaxed, your stomach in and butt sticking out like a duck. It's very odd and I can't seem to get it. The side poses and front pose are easy enough. Apparently, I'm supposed to smile during this process too. And wear 5" heels. And a bikini. *What have I gotten myself into?*

Finally Daniel says, "I think I'm going to outsource the rest of this to my girlfriend, Maria. She's training to compete in the nationals and can teach you more tricks than I ever could."

I set up a time to meet with Maria, and we meet in the gym locker room where it's more private. I am wearing a normal bikini and my practice heels. I haven't been able to get to the stripper shoe store yet, so I found some black 5" heels at Target. They only came in size 8, which is too big, but I had to practice with something.

"Damn! Look at those heels!" she said. She teaches me the four poses, but it's tricky, and I keep wobbling in the heels.

"Imagine you're picking up a heavy suitcase with both hands. That's right! You have to engage your lat muscles."

Again, I get a case of the giggles because posing seems so odd to me. By the end of the hour I feel like this is manageable and ask about the walk to the back.

"Walk to the back?" she asks.

"Yes, that's what they did during the Texas Shredder."

"Are you doing the bikini or the figure competition?"

"I'm doing the one for old people who have no business entering a bodybuilding competition."

"Bikini is for more soft looking bodies, and figure is for more muscle tone," she says.

"Which one are you doing?" I ask her.

"Figure," she replies.

"Well, then I need to learn the bikini moves. I can't compete with you. Look at you. Look at me. There's no way I would even have a shot in hell of placing. After killing myself and dropping thirty-five pounds. I want to at least pretend that I can hold my own against other senior citizens."

So now Maria is outsourcing me to another gal, to teach me the bikini poses, which are **completely different** than the figure poses. *Who knew there would be so much to this?*

Apparently the key to placing in the bikini competition is having a toned body combined with a lot of swagger. I can't speak for the body yet (I'm still working on my predisposed genetic pot belly), but I can totally pull off swagger. I'm a Jersey Girl after all. We have attitude.

Tonight I plan to watch some You Tube videos to see what I can learn about the bikini poses before my sassy swagger lesson with the newest person.

I will channel my inner Sex Goddess . . .

CAN I TAKE STEROIDS?

Daniel waves me over off the stationary bike and I sit down at the leg press. He puts 90 lb. on the machine and I begin to lift with my legs.

"So . . . I was eavesdropping at Texas Shredder last week . . ." I said, not exactly glancing at him. (1 . . . 2 . . . 3 reps on the press . . .)

"Oh?" (4 . . . 5 . . .)

"And two women were talking about this great supplement called _____. The one said it really jump-started her workouts—"

"Come on, push through your heels." (7 . . . 8 . . .)

"—and recommended it to the other woman, and wondered why she wasn't taking it already." I finish reps 11 and 12, lock out, and place my feet on the ground. "So when can I take that?" I asked looking at him point blank.

He paused before speaking. "That's a steroid, and you won't be taking that." Neither of us said anything for a moment as we stared at each other.

"But how am I supposed to compete against these other women who are taking steroids when I'm not?" I asked quietly.

"You're not going for your pro card; you just want to walk on the stage. Not everybody does it . . ." he said shrugging it off.

"Yeah, but I don't want to look stupid on the stage! You saw those women in the competition. Look at them . . . look at me . . ." My gaze drifts down to my stomach in scrutiny. It looks like an accordion from the stretch marks of childbirth.

Why did I ever think I could do this? Maybe I should quit.

"You told me to train to win," I challenged. "How can I ever hope to win anything if all these other people have an unfair advantage?"

He leaned in, his arm resting against the weights. "You *do* have to train to win. But whether you *actually* win is another thing entirely."

I exhale. *It figures I'm training with the one bodybuilder on the planet who doesn't do steroids.*

"How much weight did you lose since we started?"

"Well, on January first I was one hundred fifty and this morning I was one hundred twenty."

"Look, everything you're doing here you can be proud of. You dropped thirty pounds, you're building muscle, and you did everything through diet, exercise and a few supplements. Don't do steroids."

I start the next set (1 . . . 2 . . .), focusing on my old sneakers pressing against gravity. Thinking about my old body . . . going to be onstage in merely *weeks* against younger bodies . . . *Why are they taking drugs? I need them more than the other women do.*

"Hey, I'm in the same boat you're in with my next competition," he offers.

"You're thirty-eight and had two C-sections?"

He smirks in response. (5 . . . 6 . . .)

"No drug testing at my next show. I'm competing against guys who are stacking steroids all day long, but I'm not. (9 . . . 10 . . .) *And neither will you.*"

(11 . . . 12. Done.) He's right, after all. What kind of example would I be setting for my children if I chose to win at the cost of cheating?

"Well, I guess 'roid rage' would not work so well with the other mommies on the playground," I smiled.

"Yeah. Plus, you're already pretty aggressive with all the 2Pac you listen to."

Regina: Just read your blog post.
Lisa: Oh?
Regina: I don't care how strong you are right now, if you do steroids I will kick your ass!
Lisa: I'm not doing steroids.
Regina: Better not be!
Lisa: Don't worry, my trainer talked me down from crazy.
Regina: Good

LA ROGUE

I am on a mission to get myself those heels. I asked Regina if she wanted to come with me to La Rogue, but she declined. Shopping at La Rogue is turning out to be quite an ordeal. I have my kids with me since I was expecting something along the lines of a Hot Topic type clothing store, but La Rogue is, you know, an *adult* store. *Oops.*

So I have to describe to the clerk the shoe I want (clear, 5" heel minimum) and she brings it outside to me while I'm waiting with my kids.

After my $65 investment and spending a week trying to walk in these things, I have new respect for strippers. I also had a posing lesson with Dave Goodin (aka Mr. Texas Shredder himself!) and he told me the shoes were wrong. I had indeed purchased, you know, actual stripper shoes.

So if you are new to figure and bikini competitions, please learn from my mistake. Let's look at the two types of shoes and note some differences:

GOOD HEEL (USED FOR BODYBUILDING COMPETITIONS)
- o Has 5″ heel
- o Has a strap to give your ankle support. (The strap isn't required, it's just helpful.)
- o Sole of shoe is close to ground

BAD HEEL (USED FOR . . . WELL YOU GET IT)
- o Has 6″ heel
- o No strap
- o Has 1″ platform sole

Later this week I'm back at the gym, talking with one of the older women in the locker room who had recently retired. She asked me how my week was and I told her that I made not one, but two, trips to La Rogue.

"Oh yeah, that's where all the strippers go."

Why am I the only person in Austin who didn't know about this place?

LOSING MY MIND . . . AND KEYS

I can always tell when my husband drives my car because he messes up the seat and all the mirrors and changes the radio station on me. As I adjust everything back to their proper coordinates, I listen to a comedian on the radio. (Henri was listening to Laugh USA on Sirius, apparently.)

"My father, he just keeps losing his keys." *I feel your father's pain, Mr. Comedian.* "He can't remember if he left them on the kitchen table or on the desk. I mean he was *always* losing his keys. So last year, my brothers and sisters, we all chipped in and put him in a home."

I started laughing, not just because it was a funny bit, but because I think my family is about to put me in a home too. I'm not sure if it's the reduced-carb diet, or the supplements, or the general exhaustion from working out so much, but I am forgetting *everything* lately.

At various times over the past two weeks I have neglected to pack in my gym bag: my socks, a water bottle, a bra to wear after my shower, sneakers (I was on the treadmill in boots that day), my weight lifting gloves, and I remembered my iPod but forgot the headphones.

My home life was not much better. I would walk into a room full of vigor and purpose and once inside the room have absolutely no idea why I was there. It felt like "baby brain," which is when you're pregnant and can remember nothing. So to help myself I would say whatever I was looking for aloud until I saw it. But that didn't always help and it made me seem like a crazy person who talks to herself and owns 100 cats. (Don't worry—I have no pets; just children.)

But today is different. Today, I am in command of my mind. I have Rylee fully dressed, fed, and getting into the car with her lunch packed in her Disney Princess backpack. Go me. Little Henry is also dressed and fed and thankfully he gets into his car seat without struggle. We leave practically on time and I give myself a big mental high five.

We arrive at school only five (OK—seven) minutes late. Rylee gets out of the car and I unhook Henry to discover he is wearing socks but not shoes. *Oops.* I carry him in hoping no one notices my slight oversight. Rylee is wearing her ladybug dress and looks adorable.

But her dress is nothing compared to what all the other kids are wearing. Yes, Mother of the Year here forgot it was Pajama Day.

And I could not help thinking, *Oh my God, can't they just go to school and learn to read and add? Why do I have to remember Pajama Day too? I bet kids in China don't have Pajama Day!*

I guess I'll just have to take that herb that helps your memory . . . *now what was that herb called?*

MY BODY IS A SCIENCE PROJECT—CLIMATE CHANGE

I'm at the gym, and Daniel is asking me a question.

"Do you have an addictive personality?"

"No, not really. Why?"

"Because it's time for you to take fat burners. You don't have to take them. If you have an addictive personality you *shouldn't* take them," said Daniel sternly.

"What are they? Like Xenadrine EFX?" *I took that one before.*

"One type is like that, the other is a thermo enhancer. The directions say you can take two pills twice a day, but that's not what I want you to do. I want you to take one pill from the thermo on the first day, and then take one pill from the EFX on the next day. At the end of the month take a week off from both. Take them only in the morning, after your workout, with food. Don't take them after two o'clock or you'll be up all night. Also, they will probably make your body temperature rise. Lifting weights in general will raise your body temp, so don't be surprised if you get night sweats. Any questions?"

"Nope."

Fat burners! I get to take fat burners! This will eliminate my pot belly once and for all. Yahoo!

I've asked my other friends at the gym and checked some websites and apparently fat burners are the norm in the bodybuilding world for both men and women during the final 12 weeks before competition.

Today is the first day I tried the thermo fat burner, and apparently, I did it wrong. (Are you surprised?) I took one and then my skin turned all patchy and red and felt prickly all over, so I figured I was having an allergic reaction and took an allergy pill.

I got to the gym and told Daniel about my allergic reaction.

"That's not an allergic reaction, the flushing is from the niacin."

"Oh. Well, why didn't you tell me it would do that?"

"I thought you said you took fat burners before."

"Well not one that set my skin on fire!"

"You know my number. If anything weird is going on with your body, just text me before you start self-medicating. Don't be embarrassed, or think that something is too gross to talk about, or whatever. Just talk to me."

Daniel wasn't kidding about the temperature rise. It reminds me of what I felt after I gave birth and my hormones were leveling out. I've come back from working out at the gym. Big Henri takes Rylee to school and it's just me and Little Henry.

The wind is blowing outside and I'm exhausted from doing my lifting. Fortunately for me, Little Man is tired because he's been up since just after I left at 4:30 a.m., something his father enjoyed immensely, I'm sure. I turn on the AC because it's so hot, and we both lie on my bed to take a nap.

The wind is blowing a lonely sound, like a mourning woman, and I think of the Adele *21* CD as I begin to doze. Thirty minutes later I wake up shivering. I'm freezing now and turn off the AC. Henry is still asleep and I quietly wrap myself in my favorite gray Abercrombie & Fitch sweatshirt. (OK—it's my husband's sweatshirt; I've just commandeered it.)

I'm still tired and take advantage of Henry's slumber. My teeth are chattering; the wind is knocking against my bedroom windows. It sounds angry, like the big bad wolf about to blow the house in. I feel like I'm in that scene in Star Trek where the bad guy keeps changing the temperature, first freezing the crew and then making them swelter.

The fat burners did not make my stomach flat, but they do make me appreciate central air conditioning. Also, the pills have a ton of caffeine in them, and once the caffeine kicks in, in a nutshell: HI! I'M AWAKE NOW!

And then, when the caffeine wears off: ZZZZ!!!

SAUNA TALK—PART 2

Remember how the first time I went into the sauna everyone pretty much ignored me and went back to talking about pigs?

9-1/2 Weeks Later . . .

I bust into the sauna room and quickly strip off my drenched sweatsuit, and I don't give a rat's ass who's looking. I have EXACTLY 11 minutes to stretch, wipe myself down with a towel, and get to the training desk; otherwise, Daniel will call me out again.

Underneath, I'm wearing a shirt that says "Boys are Stupid" and black Nike shorts, and I put my hair in two pigtails just like Pink Hair Lady does. I look ten years younger than I did three months ago. I begin doing the downward facing dog yoga stretch.

The room is apparently filled with men, who have paused their conversation to watch my whirlwind of activity. I seem to have interrupted the punch line of some dirty joke one of them was telling.

I do lunge stretches, alternating my feet, then slowly rise up, one vertebrae at a time.

After a brief hesitation, one man says, "And that's when the donkey kicked!" The other men laugh a bit uncomfortably.

"Yeah, those shows they have in Mexico are not particularly civilized," said one man in apology.

"But those are the most fun ones to go to," I say devilishly. The men all burst out in relieved laughter.

"I wasn't sure if I should end the story—I didn't want to offend you."

Another man said, "I think she would be offended if you didn't tell it dirty."

"Oh you have *no idea*," I say dangerously, bending back over into downward facing dog.

Suddenly the room is silent and I smile to myself. Then I mention my husband and kids and the tension is broken again.

But for an instant it was fun commanding the room.

I head to the trainer desk, but Daniel's not there. Odd. So I go to the locker room and see that he sent me a text.

Daniel: Am sick. Can't train today.

Love and Attraction "Easy, Trigger," says Henri, his eyes narrowing as I tell him about the sauna talk.

"I mean, we're still talking farm animals with pigs and donkeys, but *my* how the context has changed," I say.

"Dropping ten dress sizes will do that," he says, taking a sip of his coffee from his San Diego mug.

"Oh, Henri, you know how married people are. We come close to the line, and then retreat into the safety of conversations about spouses and kids. I told them how supportive you were about this whole competition."

Henri looks over my attire. He seems a little at war with his own reaction. "Someone said to me, 'Aren't you worried that Lisa lost so much weight? Aren't you getting jealous?' 'No,' I said. Isn't that crazy someone would say that?" he laughed, but the laugh didn't reach his eyes.

I put my gym bag down on the kitchen table. I say nothing. I rinse out my water bottle with the leftover protein powder and think. See, he said some pretty mean shit to me when I was fat. *I will always love you*, he said last November, *I'm just not attracted to you right now.*

Sometimes I just wish I'd met him when I was fat. If he'd dated me while I was fat, at least I'd know that he loved me for *me*—my personality— and not for me + my body, with a stress on thin body.

He said to me once, "When you shovel food into your mouth it's like you're saying, 'I hate you, Henri.'"

I have food issues—don't get me wrong—but a lot of the crap he throws my way has nothing to do with me and everything to do with him and his own hang-ups. I bought into a lot of his crap for years. But now that the haze is beginning to leave me, some things are changing inside me.

I will always love you too, Henri.

But now that I am thinner, more confident, and in the best shape of my life, now I direct a critical eye in *your* general direction. Yes, I will always love you too, but perhaps I'm not as attracted to you right now.

But I say nothing. Because the truth is, I'm still attracted to him. He never changed shape, after all; I did. I've loved him since I was 25. He is my rock and he makes me laugh constantly. And I could end his moment of uneasiness and nervousness right now by saying as much.

But I say nothing.

I allow him to experience this discomfort so that in my silence he might feel a glimpse of the tender ache I felt when I heard his rejection of me. I wonder if this touch of anxiety might lead him to realize that even though I will always love him, attraction is a two-way street and sometimes it's based on more than looks.

We both feel the tension of my silence.

"I don't have to start going to the gym so I can kick someone's ass do I? I mean it would take me two weeks to get in shape, but I have good muscle memory."

"No, you don't need to kick anybody's ass, and yes, you should come to the gym. Come work out with me."

"I don't have the time."

"That's an excuse. Make the time."

"My membership expired."

"I can get you a free weekly pass," I say, walking back to our bedroom. I take off my clothes and step into the shower. He is watching me, but I ignore him. I haven't felt this powerful in years.

He begins shaving over the sink now. "I think it's good you're flirting," he says after a pause. "It's healthy for the ego."

"Of course you would say that. You're a flirt."

He is. He is a born salesman, and can make anyone feel like the most important person in the entire world.

Once we were at a party at the Polo Club in San Diego, and Henri was literally surrounded by very thin, very lovely, rich women with fake boobies, all laughing at his jokes. "Oh, Henri," they cooed.

A mutual friend of ours was standing next to me. "Doesn't that bother you, the way he flirts like that?"

"Not really. If I wanted to, I could get him to come over to me in less than a minute without saying a word."

"Really?" she said, eyes arching at my boast.

I looked around the crowd and saw a nice-enough looking man sitting at a table, fumbling with a camera. There was no ring on his finger. I sat down next to him.

"Excuse me, I see that you are a photographer. That's so interesting.*"*

"Oh, I'm just a novice, really," he said, smiling. I proceeded to ask him questions about his camera, which he enthusiastically answered, laughing and smiling progressively, eager to share information about his passion for photography.

"Hey, baby," said Henri sliding next to me, his arm loosely landing over my shoulders. I looked at my friend. Her mouth was dropped open and she raised her glass to me.

I know my man.

As I proceed to lather my hair, my thoughts keep drifting back to San Diego. . . .

. . . Back to the restaurant on the rooftop where he told me, "You're never going to lose the weight and you haven't even had a baby yet!" He was angry I was eating a second roll with butter. The funny thing was, I don't even like rolls, I just ate it to piss him off. It worked.

Who the hell was he to tell me what I could or couldn't eat? It's my body, not his. Why was he always so shallow? Wasn't I the same person inside, no matter how my body looked? He was blessed with an insanely fast metabolism and is thin through no effort of his own. He never would understand my plight with weight, or the frustrations surrounding going on a diet, or running marathons—marathons!—in an attempt to look toned and still never quite succeeding.

My body would never be small enough for him, so he used words to cut me down to size. It worked.

"Lisa, I'm just so proud of you," he said, interrupting my thoughts. "Your confidence is back, and that's sexier than hell. Of course men are going to flirt with you."

The terry cloth towel I use to dry my hair is striped with burgundy and tan lines and a thin brown line every so often. I wrap myself in it, so I'm not naked. I'm still standing in the shower.

"It's different now," I said evenly.

"How's that?"

"You're different. In the past you used to say things—mean things—about my weight."

"I haven't said anything about your weight inages. I learned you're going to do what you want to do anyway, so I just stay out of it."

"Let me finish. You used to say mean things, but this time it's different. This time, you're supportive, and it feels so good to hear you say you're proud of me."

"Well, I am." His expression tells me he's kind of taken aback.

I step out of the shower, out of my glass walls. "But what if I gain all the weight back?" My eyes are welling up, but I'm fighting the tears.

"I'll love you whatever weight you are. I've proven that already haven't I?"

"Yes," I shrug.

"But I don't think you're going to gain it back this time because *you're* different this time, and I can see it. Maybe that's why I'm more supportive. Something clicked in you and you're back to yourself again. You got your mojo back. Don't cry." He hugs me.

"Plus, I used to love bodybuilding when I was in my 20s. It was a time in my life I felt strong and in command, so I like hearing about your training. It makes me nostalgic and makes me live a little vicariously though you."

The kids are running in the room now, life's demands interrupt again, but it's nice sharing a moment with my husband after not talking, not *really* talking, for so long.

WAIT, WEIGHT, WAIT

I'm a second child. Even though my mother always said that my brother and I got everything equally, deep down I knew the truth: first kids have it better. First kids don't have to share their parents' attention with anyone. Second kids are born waiting in line.

I hate waiting. So does my son, my second born child. "Now my turn!" he says, convinced we will deprive him of something unless he demands his fair share.

For instance, I will pour Rylee some milk.

"Now my turn!"

Or turn on the TV.

"Now my turn!"

Yesterday Rylee came home sick from school.

"Now my turn!" Henry said.

"Henry, that doesn't even make any sense! I'm sick. Why would you want to be sick?" Rylee is utterly frustrated with him.

"Now my turn! I sick!" he cried.

His impatience is beginning to spread. I hate going to the gym when it's crowded, especially with weekend warriors who lollygag instead of doing things efficiently. Or like, when I ask to work in a set and the woman is like, "No, I'm using this now." Like she OWNS the 15 lb. dumbbells. And all the machines are full, so when I finish a set I have to hunt down another piece of equipment that isn't being used, and is in the correct muscle group of my split that day.

Not only am I impatient, I'm a carb-depleted bitch and I'm ready to bite the head off of the next person who gets in my way.

I tell Daniel about it at our next session and my voice keeps getting louder and louder, like from my Off Broadway days, because I'm just so pissed off about the situation.

"Daniel, I'm at the gym on Saturday and this guy was hogging the smith machine, and he didn't even know what he was doing! His form was all wrong! And I had places to be and I'm all like, 'Back off you punk assmotherf***er, I've got squats to do!' I mean, I didn't say it, but I thought it! I guess it's good I'm not on steroids after all, because I was ready to punch the guy!"

You know that look that a 13-year-old boy gives his mom when she is totally embarrassing him at the mall in front of his friends? Yeah, that's the look Daniel was giving me as he tried to quiet me down.

"Ease up on the 2Pac, killer."

TIME MANAGEMENT

I hand the cashier at Coffee Bean a $2 bill.

"Wow, I haven't seen that in a while."

"I know. It's pretty rare. I was going to keep it but it's all I have in my wallet and the chance for me to drink a cup of coffee in peace is even rarer, so it's worth it."

My large cup of coffee is ready in seconds and I pull the vanilla extract out from the Ziploc baggie in my purse and pour it in. It's not as good as creamer but has 0 calories and is on Daniel's approved list of self-indulgent food substitutions.

While sitting down at the mini coffee table my husband calls, spoiling my idyll. He wants to continue our argument about this morning.

"We can't continue Thursday mornings like this. I have to do everything and it's stressing me out! Thursday is supposed to be my morning off and I can't relax because you can't get out the door on time." His righteous indignation is in full swing and I haven't even been able to sip my coffee yet.

His beef? He has to dress the kids and feed them cereal.

I know! The hardship! The audacity of me to ask him to feed and dress his own children one day a week! How dare I????

In theory, Thursdays are the best day of the week for me. Know why? Because Rylee is at nursery school until noon and Little Henry goes to a two-hour toddler Spanish class . . . a *drop off* Spanish class . . . meaning one day a week I get two hours to do whatever the heckI want. Yahoo!!

Henri views this as his morning off too because I'm the one taking Rylee to school and not him. He gets to do whatever the heck he wants to do until 1 p.m. when we come home. In my view he gets the better end of the bargain, but I'm happy for the theoretical "relaxation" time.

In reality, Thursdays are unduly stressful.

My Thursday mornings entail me waking at 4:25 a.m. to get my Arctic attire on, get to the gym, do 50 minutes of cardio, then 50 minutes of weight lifting. Henri got annoyed with me showering at the gym because it got me back home at 7:15, so now I shower at home to placate him but still he feels it's his duty to tell me the time every two minutes as I try to lather and rinse.

"It's 7:05, Lisa. . . . It's 7:07, get out of the shower. . . . It's 7:09!"

OH SHUT THE F*** UP AND LET ME WASH!

Sometimes my son will want to join me, which extends the cleaning timeline further. "Now my turn!" he'll say, ripping off his clothes and jumping in. So then I get to wash him too. If, God forbid, I try to shave my legs both Henrys will find need to comment. Big Henri will say, "You don't have time to shave! It's 7:13! Get out of the shower!" Little Henry will say, "Now my turn!" and put his leg up so I can pretend to shave his leg too.

"Oh? You're going to be a bodybuilder, Little Man?" I laugh. "Real men shave their legs, huh?" Bodybuilders shave *everything* apparently. Hee hee.

I dry off the baby and put a diaper on him, sending him off to Big Henri for clothes while I dry and dress. I didn't even wash my hair. Thank God for baseball caps.

Henri is shouting the time at me. "It's 7:25! I guess it's just all me getting the kids ready! And I need three months of our bank statements and a letter to the tenant that we're going to enter her unit to do routine maintenance on Monday. I told you I needed this last week."

OK, my bad, it totally slipped my mind he needed those things, so now we're both scrambling and I have the added bonus of feeling defensive too.

I hurl crackers and Craisins® and chicken slices in Ziploc baggies and put them in each child's lunch bag. I down my 10,000 supplements and cook up my Meal 1 food. While it's cooking I fling the lunch bags in the car, grab my computer and put that in the car, chuck my food on a paper plate and toss that on the front seat with a plastic fork as Henri puts Rylee's hair in a ponytail and continues yelling at me.

I'm so sick of him yelling that I yell back, "Will you relax?!! She's four years old! It's nursery school. They play with Play-Doh the first fifteen minutes anyway. Who cares if we are five minutes late?! Plus, I'm driving, you're not. Just relax!"

Now he's mad at me for yelling back at him in front of the kids. Somehow his yelling at me in front of the kids was totally fine. Oh whatever, Mary.

But now I'm sitting at The Coffee Bean and blogging about how annoying my husband is and it's making me feel better. And right at this moment I'm sure he is thinking about how annoying I am too. He has a point; we do need better traffic flow.

OK, so here's the **Time Management Plan**.

1. I'm making up a chore chart so Rylee can get herself dressed in the morning. I'll teach her how to put a ponytail in her own hair. She's a smart girl. I know she can do it.
2. I'll lay out Little Henry's clothes the night before. That seems to work.
3. I'll pre-pack the little Ziploc bags full of nonperishable snack foods like crackers and nuts so they are easy grabs from the pantry.
4. I'll place the cereal bowls, spoons, etc., on the kitchen table the night before. All Henri will have to do is add milk.
5. Henri needs to wake up earlier. If I can get up at 4:25, he can wake up 15 minutes earlier if that helps him get in a better frame of mind to (God forbid!) dress and feed his own children one day a week.

Wish me luck pulling this off for the next eight weeks. I think this will work better because everybody (including the kids) will be pitching in.

Two hours later, I head back to Olas Spanish school, pick up Little Man, and pray that he falls asleep so I can take a nap myself. I turn on the Music Together CD and everything, but the dude just won't sleep, so we drive over to Central Market and chase ducks for awhile. Mostly I'm chasing my son and making sure he doesn't fall in the pond.

I'm one of those moms who's OK with her kids getting dirty. I let him splash in the puddles and pick up rocks from the mud and we both crouch down in the marshy area to spy on the turtles. He's fairly filthy but satisfied and I wipe him down as best I can with the diaper wipes and then head over to pick up Rylee.

She is chatting on about some four-year-old drama in the sandbox and requests the Spanish CD and her favorite song, "La Noche." Between my lack of sleep, sore muscles, slow-moving traffic on Lamar Blvd., and the lullaby sung by some soothing Spanish lady, I fell asleep. Behind the wheel. With my kids in the car.

Someone honked their horn at me and I jolted awake, my heart throbbing. *Holy shit, I could have killed my kids. Or someone else's kids.*

I turned the CD off, switched the music to a rock station, and rolled down the window to get some air in.

Rylee said, "But I want 'La Noche' . . ."

"No! Mommy needs to stay awake!" I shouted back, my hands trembling on the wheel. Rylee started to cry because I almost never yell, which made me feel worse. I dig through the console and find some gum to chew.

"I'm sorry, honey, I shouldn't yell. I just need a faster song."

We get home and I pull everyone in bed and take a nap.

The next day it's Friday and I meet Daniel at the trainer desk. I've already done my cardio, which usually calms me, but I'm still shaken from yesterday's events, which got even worse, if you can imagine.

Today is back/bicep/abs day, but we only do the back and bicep part. I have to do abs on my own. I'm doing alternating rows with 35 lb. weights.

"Everything OK?" he asks.

"No, everything is not OK. Nothing is OK."

"What's wrong?"

"Henri's pissed I'm spending so much time at the gym, a collection agency is calling me about hospital bills, two tenants moved out, Little Henry won't freaking use the potty even though I know he knows how to do it and yesterday I fell asleep behind the wheel! I could have killed my kids!"

"Whoa. Calm down."

"I'm sorry, I don't mean to vent."

"No, it's OK. Get it out. That's why I'm here."

"No, that's not why you're here. I'm sorry to dump my problems, I'm just so incredibly frustrated with my life right now."

"Is there anything I can do?"

"No, of course not."

"You need more sleep."

"I know."

"I checked your food journal. You're not eating enough. Are you trying to cut calories?"

"No, I'm just falling asleep. The fat burners wake me in the morning, but then I crash really hard in the afternoon. I'm so tired that I go to bed for an hour as soon as Henri gets home, but then I have to wake up to put the kids to bed. And then I'm just up. It's the only time I get to hang out with Henri."

"Can you take a nap?"

"If my son cooperates I can."

"Take some B12. That will give you some energy. Make up your food ahead of time and maybe have Henri put it next to the bed, wake you up and then run away."

I start to laugh. "Yeah, I'm pretty bitchy when I wake up apparently."

"Force yourself to eat. And force yourself to go to bed earlier."

"I told Henri what happened and he said if I'm feeling too tired to drive to just call him."

"That's good."

"I'm already imposing on his time so much with this competition."

"Eight weeks from now it'll all be over. No more going to the gym twice a day. Your diet will loosen up. I think you need a 'me' day, Lisa. You're really stressed out. Take this weekend off as rest days and just give yourself a break."

"But I'll mess up my whole workout routine."

"You're far enough out. Take a break."

I exhale. I feel embarrassed this has become a therapy/bitch session, but mostly I feel like a weight has been lifted off my shoulders because I have a strategy to get over this hurdle.

ME DAY

My best friend from childhood, Meghan, gave me a one-hour massage gift certificate for my birthday. She said she was inspired that I was entering the competition and sticking with it, and should use it to soothe my sore muscles. I love Meghan.

I also love massages, 'cause it's a massage, right?

This place was very she-she. They had the clean white furniture with the cherry wood accents. A water feature was making this gentle splashing sound as it trickled down the gray slate. Orchids were delicately hanging over the side of an olive-colored pot. All I could think was, *Holy Hell my kids would destroy this place in a heartbeat.* That gave me the giggles.

Have you ever had the giggles in a really high-end snooty place? Everyone had perfect hair and perfect nails and designer sunglasses that were just slightly too big for their faces, and here I was giggling to the point of tears. I think I actually snorted. I have the most embarrassing idiosyncrasy of laughing at inappropriate moments.

Anyway, I follow my massage with a trip to Lady Bird Lake. I sit at a picnic table and just write out blogger challenge posts (which I am gravely behind on, apologies to Fitness Cheerleader!) It was so wonderful to just be able to write!

And the even better news? Henri found a babysitter, so he joins me downtown. Since I recently hit a huge milestone of losing 30 pounds, I decide to get in touch with my former wild side and re-pierce my navel. I removed the ring during my first pregnancy because once my bellybutton popped out the navel ring reminded me of the ring between an ox's nostrils, and who wants to look at your own tummy and say, "Toro"?

While happy in spirit with my new bellybutton ring, the reality was pretty evident: I'm not 25 anymore. The top part of my abs look pretty good, but the lower half has what's known as "Mom's Apron." When a woman is pregnant, obviously the skin over her stomach stretches to accommodate. If you're a lucky winner of the Great Genetics Pool, your skin returns to normal. If you are a member of the other 90% population (aka—My Genetics

Pool Has An Odd Sense of Humor) you get Mom's Apron. It doesn't go away without surgery. (That was one thing I actually did do research on.) *Sigh.*

Oh well, at least I went on a hot date with my husband and my bellybutton ring looks good if I wear high-waisted pants.

DSST: CAN I STARVE MYSELF?

This is a really weird process for me, training for a competition. Hands down I look the best I've ever looked in my entire life, and I mean ever, ever.

But.

But . . .

But my best isn't close to being good enough, in my opinion, to looking like those women I saw onstage at the Shredder. And even though I see the results of trusting Daniel and following the meal plan, I just can't shake my fears.

Henri said he was reading an article online about some Victoria's Secret model (it's OK—she was on his Celebrity Circle list), and she described the diet she does before doing the televised lingerie show. Of course, I had to look this up and print it out for Daniel. (See how helpful I am?)

She doesn't eat any solids for two weeks before the show, just drinks protein shakes. That sounds like a good idea to me, but to Daniel? Not so much.

"That is a different thing entirely than what you're doing, Lisa," he said reading the print out.

"But it makes sense doesn't it? No wonder her stomach is so flat."

"Your stomach will be flat too, but you'll be eating food six times a day."

"Really? Even the day before the show?"

"You'll be eating the day of the show too."

"No way! Really? They did not eat the day of the competition!"

He assured me they did, but it was just fewer calories in the final weeks.

The more I fixated on her diet plan, the more I convinced myself it would be a good idea. Later that day I send him a text.

Lisa: Are you sure you don't want me to try that diet? 'Cause I'm totally cool with starving myself. I did the cayenne pepper lemonade cleanse and that was only 600 calories per day and I did it for 10 days straight. Twice. Seriously, it will bring back nostalgia for my acting days.

Daniel: NO!!!!!!!!!!!!

That's a new record for exclamation points.

Daniel: Are you following your meal plan?
Lisa: Yes.
Daniel: Are you following your exercise split?
Lisa: Yes.
Lisa: I'm doing my cardio 50 minutes plus 30 more before we meet. I'm stretching for 10 minutes every day. I'm wearing my sweatshirt. I haven't cheated on the diet once since before the Shredder. I'm doing those top secret things you told me to do. I'm doing absolutely everything you told me to do.
Daniel: Then calm down and trust the process. You will NOT starve yourself. You will follow the meal plan and you will be ready for the show. How are you going to lift weights if you have no calories? This is not a binge and diet thing, it's a lifestyle choice.
Lisa: OK
Daniel: You will be ready. Trust me.
Lisa: OK. Sorry.

I GOT NO GAME

I was never really into the club scene, or bars for that matter either, probably because wearing short skirts and dancing lustily were not my strong suits. No, most of my dates came from friend introductions and led to dinners where I attempted to impress the opposite sex with snarky remarks and sexual innuendos. That usually did the trick.

But now that I'm in a bikini competition no one gives a darn about my witty mind; it's completely about how I move my body. Here's the utter truth: I got no game.

Daniel's girlfriend, Maria, got me in to take posing lessons with *her* coach, Adela Garcia. You caught that, right? *Adela. Garcia.* The woman whose name is on the competition I'm entering. The woman who is a seven-time Ms. Olympian. The woman who has a team of bikini, figure and fitness champions. And not even *she* can fix my lame-ass posing!

In posing class it became painfully apparent that I didn't know how to rotate my hips, walk with elongated legs, or thrust out my chest in general, let alone do it with 5" stripper heels. Adela told me, "Stick your ass out and make those heels your bitch."

Um . . . but I'm from the suburbs . . . *This is so embarrassing!*

Daniel asks me how it's going (which, of course, he already knows, because his girlfriend is in the class with me), and I confess my attempt at being sassy is a hot mess. Daniel tells me to try dancing.

So I go to Walmart (big shocker) and buy a *Sizzling Salsa* dancing DVD. Ever try to do a sizzling salsa exercise video when you have a 2-1/2-year-old in the house? I'm certainly not going to dress lasciviously in front of my children, so already my libido is reduced some by wearing sweatpants and a T-shirt. Even though I try to do this while Little Henry takes a nap—(what a joke! Henry never naps!) he still manages to come in front of the TV and either hugs my legs, or lifts my weights and runs into another room with them.

Plus, it just isn't carnal enough. So I return to Walmart, and purchase the more risqué *Cardio Strip Tease* DVD. I practice the moves at 5 a.m. when everyone is sleeping . . . that helps.

Maria gives me the best advice though: "Practice your poses in front of your husband. He'll let you know if you're doing it right."

Hmm . . .

It's 9 p.m. and the children are sleeping. I'm in bikini and hooker heels and Henri resides on the couch as I prance and pose in front of him.

"You know, this sport is really growing on me," Henri says smiling a devilish grin. "All you need now is a whip, and we can really have some fun."

Arching my back to accentuate my curves, I slowly saunter over to him. Fixing my eyes in a stony stare I whisper, "If you knock me up before this competition, Traugott, I will end you."

A SILENT DISAGREEMENT WITH DANIEL

Today's Friday. Normally I meet Daniel at 6 a.m. but he's going to a wedding this weekend in Louisiana, so we decide to meet an hour earlier. He's been rearranging my training schedule because his own schedule is in flux and I decide to text him this morning at 4:30 a.m. to make sure he was going to show up, since he rescheduled this session twice on me already, once literally five minutes before start time.

Lisa 4:26 a.m.: Good morning. Cu @ 5, yes? I weigh 119!!!!!!!!!! Happy Friday

Normally he answers text messages in a nanosecond, so I'm a little nervous he is sleeping in. I am also a little annoyed at his new-found flakiness, and tired at having to wake up at 3:45 to get everything ready so I can get a half hour of cardio routine in before we meet, lest I hear the dreaded, "When I say thirty minutes of cardio that's thirty minutes, not twenty-three-ish," speech, especially if he is going to cancel on me again.

But I'm pretty happy overall because I stepped on the scale and lo and behold I weighed 119!!! It's been over a decade since I was that thin—2001 to be exact. It was the year before my father got really, really sick. I can't help but smile. I am at the traffic light, ready to turn into 24 Hour Fitness when my phone buzzes.

Daniel 4:30 a.m.: Wow! That's awesome! That's some good work! We are going to do measurements today.

Oh.

As part of Daniel's cure for my natural lack of sweating he has me do my cardio dressed like I'm preparing to descend upon the Arctic. But if I'm getting measured, that means after finishing my cardio I have to change into more normal workout clothes so I can get pinched and prodded by that fat calculator. Luckily I have extra workout clothes in my gym bag. They're getting really, really loose. Everything is going down, down, down. I'm in sheer bliss. It's better than a Hostess chocolate cupcake. And then . . .

"You're losing too much weight too fast. We need to slow that down," he says writing down numbers and doing some calculations.

Excuse me? I'm losing too much weight? This is honestly the first time ever that I heard something like that said to me.

He continued looking at all my measurement calculations, shaking his head. "You're forty-nine days out. If I reduce your calories now it won't be good. Besides, you can lose ten pounds real quick."

"Tell that to my ass," I said.

His lip quirked into a half smile and then went serious, as if preparing himself for battle with me. *"I know you are probably going to disagree,* but I want you off the fat burners starting this weekend."

"OK," I said brightly.

I don't think he heard me agree, because he continued, "So stop focusing on your weight and just trust me! And I might have to add some calories back in your diet, even though it doesn't make sense to you."

"That's fine. I trust you," I said with a smile.

He eyed me warily, obviously anticipating my patented Lisa Traugott eye roll complete with exhaling loudly in disagreement, and seemed mildly confused at the utter lack of rebellion on my part.

The truth is I *TOTALLY DISAGREE* with him; I still need to lose weight in my stomach. But he's been right about everything else thus far, so I will keep my doubts as internal dialogue and blog posts and just do what he tells me to do.

It got us to the exercise machines faster, anyway.

FOOD DREAMS #1

I'm beginning to have weird food dreams now. Last night I had a dream about eating a giant chocolate chip cookie. It was warm out of the oven, and the chips were all gooey-melty. It was the best dream ever.

DSST: YOU LOOK KINDA FAT, DANIEL

It's May, just long enough for me to forget how bad Cheater's Weekend made my body feel. But more importantly, it's almost Mother's Day and my 8th wedding anniversary, something I wasn't entirely sure I would see at one point. I want to celebrate with food.

"Can I have another Cheater's Weekend?" I ask Daniel before his next client came. (Today is Monday and my training day is Wednesday.)

Daniel looked up from the computer, surprised by my question. "Not really. When did you want one?"

"May fifteenth. It's my eighth anniversary. Also, I'd like to cheat on Mother's Day so I can have pancakes. You know, Mother's Day is the most important day of the year," I smiled.

"I'm sorry, Lisa, but May fifteenth is too close to your competition for a Cheater's Weekend. You can have a cheat meal today for dinner if you'd like," he offered.

"Never mind," I grumbled. *I don't want a cheat dinner today, I want my cheat meals when I want them. This bodybuilding diet thing is seriously getting on my nerves. Egg whites. Spinach. 3 oz. ground turkey. 1/4 cup brown rice. Fish. Repeat every f***ing day.*

"How was your weekend?" he asked.

"Fine. How was the wedding?" It was his brother's wife's sister's friend's wedding, or something sufficiently complex, and it was in Louisiana.

"It was awesome. They had all Cajun food there. Jambalaya, Gumbo, oh it was good. And I'm off-season, so I ate a lot," he smiled with a satisfied look.

"Yeah, I can tell, 'cause *you look kinda fat, Daniel.*" (I'm nothing if not passive aggressive.)

His eyes opened wide, kind of in shock, and then he chuckled. "Thanks."

Wednesday, May 9, 2012: Training Day

After completing my 30 minutes of cardio on the bike plus 10 minutes of stretching in the sauna I was at the check-in desk. Daniel had already dropped whatever weight he had gained over the weekend and his face looked normal again. Further evidence that God is a man. If I pigged out during a wedding I would be wearing it for at least half a year.

"It's leg day," he smiled.

We moved to the TRX cables. I had to hold my arms up over my head holding the cables as I did piston squats. We were making *Karate Kid* jokes.

Then he pulled out a 24" box. "Jump on this, three sets of fifteen."

"What?" It looked really high to me.

"Get out of your head and just jump on it." I did, but it scared the living shit out of me.

Then it was leg extensions: 75 lb. at 15 reps, then 5 really slow. My legs were on fire and as I rubbed my thighs he brought that damn box back over.

"Power steps. Fifteen each side."

My shirt was soaked with sweat and he just kept going: leg curls, walking lunges with a 10 lb. weight over my head, hack squat dead lift, alternating legs jumps, squats with 70lb. bar. I thought I might die.

"*I will never call you fat again, Daniel.*"

He laughed. "I forgot you even said that. Well, we're done here, but you still have fifty minutes of cardio. It's sprint day, isn't it? Wow, it really sucks to be you right now. See you Friday."

And the moral of the story is: Do not disrespect your trainer before leg day.

Our wedding, on the beach
in San Diego, CA, 2004

Baking cookies with Rylee, 2009

My father in the Air Force, 1954

Rylee Brianna, age 5

Little Henry, age 2

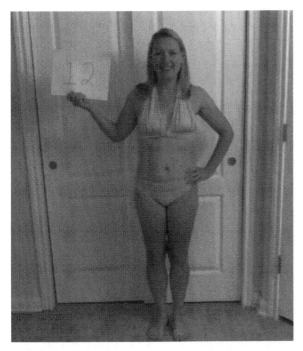

12-week countdown to the Adela Garcia Classic.

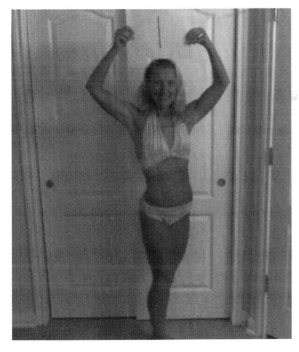

Last week before the show!

Standing with trainer, Daniel Rufini

Daniel when he's mad at me

Celebrating my 40th (yikes!) birthday with Regina, Henri, and Regina's husband, Payman

Posing at a wedding last year

Me, Rylee and Little Henry
showing off our muscles

This is me today

DSST: Can I Have Crepes?

It's now time for another episode of Dumb Shit I Said to My Trainer . . .

OK, I know Daniel said no once already, but . . . "I really, really, really want crepes for Mother's Day," I said helping Henri to unload groceries into the kitchen.

"Um, is your trainer OK with that?" asks Henri tentatively, placing a bag on the counter.

Secretly, I think Henri likes that my trainer always says no to the crap I want to eat because then it makes Daniel the bad guy, even though he's thinking the same thing as my husband.

Sometimes I also think they text each other behind my back, because they always seem to come to the exact same conclusions, albeit worded differently.

"I'll text him," I say with false enthusiasm. I didn't really want to text him; I just wanted my husband to make me the damn crepes no questions asked, but now that he dropped the "ask the trainer" bomb I guess I have to run with it.

"He's going to say no," says Henri.

"It's Mother's Day plus our anniversary and it's one meal, and I haven't cheated since March so I'm due."

2:03 p.m. Lisa: Hi. Tomorrow is Mother's Day, the most IMPORTANT day of the year. It's also just before my 8th anniversary. Can I have a cheat meal?

No response. *Is he busy, or actually considering this request? It is Mother's Day after all. He has a mother.*

2:04 p.m. Lisa: I would like crepes with raspberries, strawberries and sugar free syrup. I can use gluten free flour to make it.

Berries are practically a diet staple, right? And sugar free syrup hardly counts as anything because it's sugar free. And gluten free flour? Well, it's practically like asking my trainer if it's OK to eat a salad!

2:04 p.m. Lisa: Oh. And also, I want a cup of coffee with real creamer. Vanilla flavor.

Too much?

I put my phone on the counter and begin to put the vegetables in the refrigerator. God, I hate vegetables. Why can't chocolate be a health food? I longingly put Henri's Nestle Crunch ice cream bars in the freezer. I gaze at the phone.

No response.

The vanilla creamer was over the top, wasn't it?

I grab the phone and text my final plea like a mad woman.

2:05 p.m. Lisa: And did I mention it was Mother's Day?
2:05 p.m. Daniel: No.

"Ah, man!" I whined reading his text confirming what everyone knew was the foregone conclusion.

"Told you."

"Shut up, Henri."

2:06 p.m. Lisa: fine
2:06 p.m. Daniel: You can do whatever you want. Do I agree with it? No
2:06 p.m. Lisa: fine

I hate you, Daniel. But not as much as I hate tilapia. God, I hate fish! Egg whites, chicken, chicken, fish, fish, protein shake. Egg whites, chicken, chicken, fish, fish, protein shake. That's my life right now and I hate it.

I want crepes. I want fruit. I want a normal meal like a normal person on Mother's Day.

2:08 p.m. Daniel: Lisa, look how far you've come. U r only a few weeks out.
2:08 p.m. Lisa: I know
2:08 p.m. Daniel: U can eat as many pancakes as you want a month from now. Ur only 7 wks out and u r doing so well. Don't mess up now.
2:09 p.m. Lisa: OK Daniel. I'll eat egg whites.
2:09 p.m. Daniel: Good! U can do this!

ANNIVERSARIES

The babysitter is watching the kids and we have driven north into the Hill Country. Tomorrow is Mother's Day (the most important day of the year) and two days after that is our 8th anniversary. We decide to celebrate by just relaxing together.

Relaxing these days means putting on our exercise clothes and running along the marina at Point Venture.

"Can you believe we've been married for eight years?" I ask with wonder.

"I know, it feels like it's been forty," he says.

"You're such an a**hole!" I laugh. We circle Lake Travis and head back up the stairs by the docks. I run ahead of him.

"I hate that you're going but I love to watch you go," he says smacking my behind. I giggle and we start running through the exorbitantly expensive neighborhood, admiring the houses. They are beautifully crafted, almost like artwork; Tuscan homes, Spanish styles, old plantation styles, each more extravagant than the next.

My mind wanders to the other anniversary. My father died ten years ago this month.

"Henri, I just wanted to call to say goodbye." I stared out my apartment window, silently saying goodbye to Los Angeles too.

"Goodbye?"

"My mom called. It's not good. Dad doesn't sound right. I told Stephanie that I'm flying home tomorrow instead of Memorial Day. She's calling HR and will fill out the Family Leave paperwork for me. I told my landlord I'm probably going to move back to New Jersey."

"You're moving back home?"

"I need to take care of him. There's nothing for me here in California . . ."

My words hung between us. My acting career had slowed to a stop and Henri, the man I loved more than anyone in the world, loved me back but couldn't get beyond the hurt of his past engagement and would not commit to me fully.

We flew to Rome on Valentine's Day and everyone thought he would propose, but he didn't. I broke up with him on the plane. It was a long flight home. And now my dad was dying. I ate and ate and ate and ate from size 3 to size 9 in three months. It was the break-up diet in reverse.

"Go home to your dad. You don't have to move yet. Just see him; spend as much time with him as you can." Henri's mom died of cancer when he was 23. He knew what I was feeling.

"Someday we'll buy a lake house here," he says. He is wearing his black shirt and shorts and the sun bounces off his eyes. He is beautiful to me.

"Of course!" I say, as though buying a million dollar home was the most obvious thing in the world. I sip some water and then hand it to him. "Are you happy we are in Texas now?"

He pauses by way of drinking some water. "It's hard for me sometimes, because I've been so busy working on the property I haven't had time to make many friends. But as far as the family goes, this is the best move we ever made."

"I love it here," I say. "In a way, it reminds me of home."

People think of New Jersey as turnpikes and smokestacks but I grew up in an area surrounded by farms and forests. I used to live right next to a forest where people would go deer hunting. When I was ten, developers tore it down and built housing named Windsor Woods Condominiums. Go figure.

My father hangs up the phone. He is wearing his blue bathrobe over his pajamas and his hair is messy as ever. We don't have one picture of him on a Christmas morning without crazy hair. The couch has been pulled out to make a bed so he doesn't have to climb the stairs to his bedroom in his weakened state. He calls me to sit beside him.

"Henri just called."

"Oh?" My brows furrowed. Why was he calling my father?

"Do you love him?"

I looked down at my hands. "Yes," I replied softly.

"Why?" he asked with his gentle manner, probing without judging.

"I don't know. It just feels right. I can't explain it."

My father said nothing and seemed like he was waiting for a better explanation. His eyes were so blue and kind. He looked healthy. You would never know he was dying of cancer.

"When I was with ------- I wanted so badly for it to work. Mom thinks I should have married him. We never fought, he was kind and he loved me. But I didn't love him and when I was with him I just kept hearing my heart say, 'This is wrong, this is wrong, this is wrong.' When I'm with Henri he drives me crazy sometimes but it's passionate and he's funny and it's just . . . right. But maybe I'm not right for him. He thinks I'm going to hurt him like Joann did."

"Does he still love her?"

"No. He's just scarred by her."

We sat for a moment in silence. I stared at my hands again.

"He called me to tell me that he loves you, he's going to take care of you and he wants to marry you. You deserve to be happy, Lisa, like your mom and me."

We run up the hill, around the bend, to the vacant lot we put a bid on back on our first trip to Austin. Rylee was three months old and she was in my Baby Bjorn as we toured the city. This was a place we could live. This was a city big enough to have culture and excitement and small enough to raise a family. The sunlight dances off the lake and we hold hands walking toward the water.

"Only two more days and we will be married eight years," I say to him.

"Man, I only have two more days to scratch my seven-year itch," he teases.

"Yeah, and now that I'm a size three I guess my pool of 'mutual use' guys at the bar has increased dramatically," I reply. (I believe snarky comments by the husband should be answered by equally obnoxious comments in kind.) He laughs.

"When did you know you loved me?" I ask, throwing a stone into the water.

"Early on. You were so confident, so worldly. And you were pretty cute too. When did you know you loved me?"

My mother and I are in our new black dresses. We both gained weight and had to deal with that on top of everything else. I am outside the funeral home to get some air. I can't breathe. I can't look at my father in the coffin.

The sun is shining brightly. The beautiful day is an affront to how I feel right now. I sit on the wooden steps and begin sobbing. I sense his presence before I see him. Henri comes next to me and, even though we are broken up, I collapse in his arms and he holds me tight as the grief flows out of me.

He handles all the questions from the funeral director. He makes sure the guests are attended to at the wake and the funeral. He handles all the little details so my family can grieve in peace.

"I love you, Lisa. I'm so sorry for your loss." It was in that moment I knew he loved me, only me.

Love isn't a fancy proposal in a romantic location.

Love is showing up when you're needed without being asked.

Love is lending strength when your partner is weak.

Love is not marrying a person you can live with; love is marrying the person you can't live without.

BLOGGER CHALLENGE: WHAT IS THE PROUDEST MOMENT OF YOUR LIFE?

"Hey, fat girl!" he snarled, a grin spreading across his obnoxious face. "Fat girl, I'm talking to you!"

"She can't hear you, too much blubber in her ears," laughed his idiot twin brother.

Amanda* (not her real name) slumped lower in the seat in front of me. Her hair was long, brown, and wavy and her skin ivory white. She stared out the window and tried her best to ignore them.

The bus smelled like the gym locker room and I hated every minute of the ride. I wished that I was a trust fund baby so my parents would buy me a car and I'd never again have to listen to Dumb and Dumber.* (Not their real names, but should have been.)

The U2 *War* cassette had just finished on my Walkman, putting the comments from the two bullies into sharper focus.

"Hey, fat girl! Why are you so fat? You f***ing loser. F***ing pig." His brother started making oinking noises and they gave each other high fives.

The bus driver said nothing. She was a skinny woman in her 40s with thick glasses and stringy brown hair. Why didn't she stop this? She looked in the wide rectangular mirror above her head and scowled at the situation. But she didn't intervene. Maybe because we were in high school.

Amanda's arms were crossed over her large chest. Her shirt was too tight against her arms. The faint reflection of her blue eyes in the window looked so sad to me.

Dumber was still oinking like the pig of a person he was. "Hey, fat girl! Look at me fat girl! You f***ing fat b**ch, you—"

"Will you two just shut up?" I said slowly, surprised by the loudness and anger of my own voice.

Everyone stopped and looked at me. I never spoke on the bus. I just listened to my Walkman or did homework. I heard Amanda exhale. The bus driver said nothing, but she smiled at me in the mirror.

Then the twins turned their wrath on me. "Brainy act! F***ing brainy act! Who do you think you are?"

I put my headphones back on, only I didn't press play because I was wondering what they would say about me. They were very unoriginal. They commented on my glasses and good grades. They could not think of a farm animal that wore glasses, so I was not serenaded with barn sounds, thank God. But they kept it up, and made the bus ride hell for me for about a month. I was not inclined to stand up for myself, just other people, so I just looked out the window and wished for a car.

About a week later I was taking a walk around my neighborhood and ran into Amanda. "Thanks for sticking up for me," she said with a shy smile.

"No worries. They're just jerks," I said. But a part of me wished that I said nothing, because now all their verbal barbs were directed at me. And then the next thing she said shocked me.

"I was molested when I was seven. That's when I started gaining the weight. My therapist says that it's normal for me to do that. She said I'm hiding behind my weight so no one will look at me. She said it's OK for me to do that right now."

That stuck with me forever. So many assumptions are made about fat people. You're lazy, weak-willed, someone to be mocked. But like just about everything else, it's more complicated than that. If those twins knew what she had gone through, what it was like to be overpowered by an older man as a child, how she longed to make herself invisible to ward off that attention in the future, would they have bullied her still? If they were to walk a mile in her shoes how might they have reacted? Or is it too much to wonder if two 15-year-old bullies contained an ounce of empathy or compassion inside them?

I keep Amanda in mind when I'm inclined to say something about someone I shouldn't.

I don't always do the right thing. Or the courageous thing. But that day on the school bus I did, and it is the proudest moment of my life.

JUST A LITTLE CHANGE

I'm on my own today, doing my ab routine in the training section, and people move all around me. I like staying near the trainer cubicles because I have a clear view of the clock, and I'm out of everyone's way as they reach for dumbbells and mats.

"You're doing it wrong."

"Huh?"

Fitness Santa is next to me now. (I started calling Daniel that in my brain because he always knows if I've been bad or good.)

"You're just moving your arm up and down. You have to engage your obliques by reaching up and then twisting underneath. Try again. Feel the difference?"

"Ow! Yes."

"Do you have a minute?"

"Sure."

"Come over here."

"Oh, I brought my credit card today to sign up for more sessions."

He walks away from the trainer area and near the water fountains.

"I'm leaving 24 Hour Fitness."

"WHAT?"

"Shh!! I've given my notice and I'm going to be training at a different gym."

"Where?"

"It's a hardcore bodybuilder's gym called Metroflex. I think you'll like it."

"Where is it?"

"Nearby, in an old warehouse. It's really hardcore. There's no heat, no air conditioning, no locker rooms, just weights. But everyone who trains there competes. I'm not telling all my clients because not everyone will like that kind of place."

"Do they have childcare?"

"They don't even have showers."

"What am I supposed to do with my kids? Nursery school is done in three weeks and then they'll both be home with me all the time."

"I don't know, Lisa. Can Henri watch them?"

"I don't know. Maybe? How much is membership?"

"It's cheaper than here, thirty dollars per month I think. And my rates will drop because I'll be able to keep a higher percentage."

"Do they take credit cards? I'm doing the payment plan for sessions."

"You'll be paying me directly, so I can't do credit cards."

Now I'm feeling sick to my stomach. How am I supposed to convince my husband to pay for not one but *two* gym memberships, and oh, by the way, you'll have to rearrange your schedule to watch the kids twice a week so I can work out?

"OK, don't stress out. I can see you're stressing out. I'm still here until the end of the month to transition all my clients. If you want, I can make arrangements for you to work with a new trainer here."

"No, it's six weeks before the show; I'm not going to start with someone new who doesn't know anything about bodybuilding. That's crazy. I guess I'll just figure it out."

We both exhale. He looks relieved, but now I have a headache. I guess I have some figuring to do.

Mother's Day

I hear Henri and the kids whispering loudly to each other, banging pots and pans in the kitchen. Yes. It's Mother's Day.

I remember cooking breakfast in bed for my mother. One year I dressed up as a waitress named Shirley and took my parents' order on a Hello Kitty notebook while my brother cooked everything up.

Of course, we really didn't know how to cook anything, so we just brought up cereal and orange juice. But it was the thought.

"MY TURN!" shouts little Henry.

"No, Henry, it's *my* turn to crack the egg!" retorts Rylee, all huffy.

Glad I'm not in that kitchen! I'm secretly hoping for crepes with raspberries but Henri and the kids deliver what's on the meal plan: oatmeal and egg whites, black coffee with vanilla extract and Splenda. Henri mixed it up a little and threw in some green peppers and onions into my egg whites.

You know, even oatmeal and egg whites taste better when someone cooks them for you.

Rylee gave me a picture she made at school and a balloon with a smiley face she drew on it with a Sharpie she's not supposed to use. That kid will figure out any reason to use that Sharpie. But I love it and kiss her and little Henry who hands me a bouquet of flowers.

That's pretty much what I always wanted from Mother's Day. A picture and a hug. No crepes required.

Big Henri has an even bigger surprise. He got us tickets to see Foster the People in concert! The concert is two weeks before the show, but I think I'll be able to stick to my diet. Concert beer is always a little bit watered down anyway, so it's not like I'd be missing much.

We get the kids dressed and then head to church. This is turning out to be a pretty awesome Mother's Day after all.

ONLY A JERSEY GIRL WOULD TRY TO MESS WITH TEXAS

Every town has its own customs and social mores and I'm trying to fit in here in Texas. I've bounced around a lot (New York, London, Los Angeles, San Diego, plus back-to-back national tours), so unless I'm in my hometown in New Jersey, I always feel like I'm mildly in trouble with the locals.

Some things I heard about Texas were true. Everything is bigger here. Even the sky is bigger. And they have entire aisles in the supermarket dedicated to barbecue products and football. Also, they are polite. I hate that shit.

I don't want to be a ma'am but everyone says it here.

Excuse me ma'am? Thank you, sir! Yes, ma'am!

One time I tried to send a "yes sir" text to Daniel to incorporate the local custom, but felt like an idiot typing it, so I said f*** that I'm a Jersey girl and just wrote something poetic like "OK."

Other times, Austin is nothing like what I thought Texas would be like. For example, no one here wears cowboy hats or has an accent, which was sort of a letdown, actually. But neither my relatives in New Jersey, nor Henri's relatives in California, knew that, so for our first Christmas card we all took a picture around a Christmas tree wearing cowboy hats and put the kids on toy horses.

And then there're the natural comparisons you can't help but make after living in several locations. Like the billboards. In New York, there are billboards advertising Broadway shows; in California, there are billboards advertising TV shows; in Texas, there are billboards advertising Jesus. For real. Billboards for different churches, hashtags about exploring God, and pro-life ads.

Remember how I told you we go to Austin Stone and they have Sunday school for the kids? HYPOTHETICALLY, let's say that Little Henry got invited to a birthday party from one of the kids at Sunday school and the name on the invitation, hypothetically, was from someone with a name that wasn't gender-specific, like Dakota, or Jess.

And let's also say that, hypothetically, Mother of the Year here didn't even have a vague notion of which toddler little Jess was, but felt like a dork for asking if Jess was a boy or a girl. I scanned the invitation for more details.

The card was white with black letters (no help there) and just had a picture of a yellow cake on it with the address. *Great.*

See, I named my daughter Rylee, which is traditionally an Irish name for a boy, but instead of spelling it R-I-L-E-Y (boy name) I spelled it R-Y-L-E-E (fancy girl spelling), and when I send out announcements or birthday party invitations I make sure to pair her first name with her middle name, Brianna, so everyone knows she is a girl.

WAIT! In the inside of the card it says Jess Ashley is turning three. Whew! Dodged that embarrassment bullet!

Flash forward to today. I buy an adorable baby doll and put it in a pink gift bag with some glittery tissue paper and show up to the party. The front room is filled with presents.

Wrapped in blue.

Jess Ashley is a boy.

So I race the gift (and my kids) back to the car, pitch it in the backseat so no one sees it, come back to the party, and then make some lame excuse to the mother about forgetting the gift on our kitchen table. I feel mildly guilty that I'm totally lying at a church party. But what would Jesus do?

I text Regina.

Lisa: How can Jess Ashley be a BOY????
Regina: LOL. You're in the South now.
Lisa: What does that mean?
Regina: Gone With the Wind . . .

Freaking Scarlett! And who has a birthday party on Mother's Day anyway? Oh, it's a good thing I'm going back home to New Jersey for my reunion soon.

IT'S ALL ABOUT MONEY, HONEY

Little Henry is sick from Jess Ashley's birthday party (probably from eating too much cake and pizza), so I text Daniel I'm going to have to cancel today. I'm supposed to give a day's notice, but my son's stomach does not feel the need to provide me with any advanced warning before major catastrophes, so there's not much I can do beyond apologizing and rescheduling for later in the week.

I'm going to have to do an exercise video for my cardio because I obviously can't take him to Kids' Club either. The new gym Daniel's working at, Metroflex, has no childcare, so that means I'm going to have to keep my membership at 24 Hour Fitness for when I do the workouts on my own, and then figure out a time when Big Henri can watch the kids so I can train with Daniel. Also, I have to sign up for the new gym, pay all those fees, and have to come up with cash or check for my training sessions since Metroflex doesn't do credit cards or payment plans. But I can't really stop now; I'm seeing really good results, and I have no idea how to train for this competition on my own. It's my understanding the diet will change constantly between now and show day and if I learned anything, it's that being fit is 90% diet.

Big Henri is in a bad mood. "I can't wait until you're done with this stupid thing," he mutters as he gets dressed for work. I'm facing the mirror, changing out of the shirt my son just vomited on.

"I thought you liked the way I'm looking now," I said quietly, a hint of anger lining my voice. I step in the shower.

"Six hundred dollars for training sessions, then another six hundred dollars again, four hundred dollars for food, sixty-five dollars for heels and they're the wrong ones, eighty dollars for the 'right' ones, and you need not one but two overpriced bikinis that you will never wear again."

"Look, the competition is just six weeks away and then all these costs will disappear," I say as soothing as possible, while scrubbing my hair vigorously.

"It's not going to go away! I heard you say on the phone to your mom you were going to do another show after this one! And now you want money *to grow your blog*? Why don't you spend time on the business? WE DON'T HAVE THE MONEY FOR THIS, LISA! I keep telling you that, but you don't seem to hear me!"

I turn off the water abruptly and wrap myself in a towel.

"WE DO HAVE THE MONEY FOR THIS, BECAUSE I DON'T WANT TO GO BACK TO BEING FAT AGAIN! I WON'T!" I walk away from him, and dress quickly.

"Can't you just train yourself?"

"I don't know what I'm doing. I've never done this before. You always said you wanted a hot trophy wife, well this is the cost."

"Can't you just train without the competition part?"

"But that's the fun part!"

"Oh, so now it's about you having fun. Must be nice."

"You got to stay home with Rylee while I worked, and you had a babysitter come three times a week who did the baby's laundry, I might add. I'm home with two kids and no help, and this is the one thing in my life that's for me, and I love it!"

"So to hell with everyone else, right?"

"I wake up at five o'clock in the morning so I don't have to impact anyone with my exercise. You and the kids are sleeping."

"It's not just the exercise, it's the supplements, and the weird food, and why do you have to do another show?"

"Because this works for me. I don't want to gain the weight back."

"You won't."

"I'm not so sure."

"Lisa, you've changed your thinking. Your whole relationship with food is different now. I don't know what your trainer said to make things click, but it worked."

"So then why are you fighting me about this?"

"Because we don't have the money!"

"I've been thinking of that and I have a solution. I have fifteen thousand dollars left in my 401k. I'll take out five thousand dollars to cover all the costs of the competition, and training, and new gym, plus start-up costs for growing the blog. That way you don't have to pay a thing and I'm not taking away from any family money."

"No."

"What do you mean, 'no'? It's *my* money. I earned it before we were even married."

"You can't get it without my signature."

"IT'S MY MONEY!"

"Oh, so that's *your* money but what I make is *our* money?"

"It is *our* money. I own fifty-one percent of the building, or had you forgotten? I put up half the cash for the down payment. I was the one with the steady income. I sunk my life savings into it to float the mortgage!"

"And I'm the one working there every day!"

"Well, I would work there too if you would just stop being such a control freak! You never listen to my input, you just do whatever you want to do with the business and inform me later. How is that a partnership?"

And the screaming continued. We had a knock-down screamfest airing everything that had built up between us: resentments, jealousies, sex, money, parenting style, crap from 12 years ago.

Normally I would start crying during a fight such as this. But this time I stood toe-to-toe and shouted until I was heard. By the end of it we both had emotional battle wounds, but at least everything was in the open instead of being danced around.

He left for work. Little Henry, who was sitting on the couch watching Umizoomi, came up to me and hugged my leg.

"Hi Mommy," he said. He must have heard everything. Thank God he doesn't speak well yet. I hope he didn't understand our conversation. I sit on the couch and pull him into me.

I wish Henri and I never fought. I wish I had my own money again.

The text goes off on my phone.

Daniel: It's OK for u to reschedule this time, but I will have to charge u if u cancel without 24 hr notice next time.
Lisa: Stop bugging me about money. It's not a good time.
Daniel: Whoa. I'm not bugging u, I just have to be fair to everyone.

I don't reply. Little Henry tugs my ears and starts singing about numbers. *I just want my own money again.*

BLOGGER CHALLENGE: HOW DO YOU OVERCOME SETBACKS?

In 2000, the actor and writer unions were on strike, which meant there were no jobs to audition for, so instead I got a "real job" in the office property management industry. Basically I was a glorified receptionist taking work orders ("It's too hot/too cold/the sink is dripping, etc."). It was something I did as a temp job in New York City the prior year.

My first day on the job I tried to introduce myself to the Assistant Chief Engineer and he said, "No offense, but I'm not going to learn your name. You're the fifth receptionist in as many weeks and you look like you won't last past today."

Well, hello to you too. Game on.

In L.A., people calling my desk sounded like this: "We seem to have a bit of a *workers' comp issue* here. Genni is too cold and doesn't want to wear a sweater over her tank top."

Is that the toughest you got for me Los Angeles? Genni's worker's comp issue?

This is what I had to deal with in New York: "**It's so motherf***ing cold in here I'm ready to set the f***ing office furniture on fire! Fix it! NOW!!!**"

Needless to say I made it through my first setback and a year later not only was I still around but had been promoted to Contracts Administrator and had a Wall of Fame with 50+ customer satisfaction letters. Yet . . .

I didn't get the Assistant Manager position. **Setback!** My boss' boss told me, "Lisa, you're a smart girl but you know nothing about this industry, plus you don't have a real estate license."

I complained loudly to my then boyfriend, Henri, about the unfairness of it all. He told me, "Steel is strong because it's forged in fire."

Hmph.

So I had a baptism by fire. I was the first person at my desk in the morning and the last employee to leave at night; I volunteered for every crap job no one wanted to do if I thought it would look good on my résumé; when I wasn't working overtime or at my second job at a bar I was studying for my real estate license.

I passed the exam the first try, got employee recognition awards and every manager wanted me to work on their projects. Yet . . .

They passed on me whenever an Assistant Property Manager position came up. **Setback.** At first I could explain it away due to lack of experience, but apparently one client didn't like me and was blocking my advancement and after the third pass over I sat on a park bench by Library Tower and just sobbed in frustration.

Sometimes too many blocks in the road can mean you're on the wrong road. Henri told me to apply to other companies, but by that point I began to believe that *no one* would ever hire me for a management position. "I know you're scared to leave, but you really can do this," he said.

Secretly I applied for a job waaaay out of my league—a Property Manager position (not even assistant manager) at a 48-story high-rise. My first interview was confusing. Everyone seemed to like me except the boss' boss (we'll pretend his name was Mr. Takai). I didn't hear anything for a week and then Mr. Takai's assistant called and said he wanted to meet with me that day at 4 p.m. Fortunately, I was dressed in a nice business suit and made some excuse to my boss about going home early.

I entered Mr. Takai's office and after the briefest of pleasantries he said, "You're not qualified for this job. The only reason you're even sitting here is because you're the only candidate who rearranged their schedule to meet with me." He sat comfortably on his couch overlooking the downtown city lights in his expensive suit, expensive cologne filling the room. He was holding a drink in his hand. It looked like ginger ale but maybe it was a real drink.

My heart was racing but my anger steadied my voice. "Maybe I don't have the strongest résumé, but I'm a quick study and clearly I'm hungrier than your other candidates. My first day on the job at my current company someone told me I wouldn't last a day. Three years and fifty customer satisfaction letters later he reports to me. I'm nothing if not tenacious."

His face was a wall but his eyes studied my face, my posture, my shoes. *Thank God I polished them this morning!* "You're too young. No one will respect you," he said taking a drink.

"People don't respect an age, they respect competence. If I do a good job and know what I'm talking about, they'll trust me soon enough," I smiled, hoping lipstick was not present on my teeth.

"What are your plans for Christmas?"

Was this a job offer or polite conversation?

"It's the first Christmas since my father passed, so I'm flying home next week to be with my family."

"The job starts Friday."

Job offer!?! Or just factual information he's giving me?

"Well, I would need to give two weeks' notice. My company has been good to me and that's the professional thing to do. Plus, I need to be with my mother. But I can start after Christmas," I added quickly. My palms were sweating. I was calculating how quickly my student loans would be paid off with this management position.

"**The job starts Friday**. *If* you really want it. This is the position of a lifetime. These high-rise management jobs don't open often."

I got the job!!! But wait . . .

Setback! Why did it have to start Friday???? God, I wanted the job! $65,000 base pay plus bonus. I would practically have a corner office with *two* mahogany desks plus a secretary. It was everything I told myself I wanted, which is why I surprised myself when I said, "This is a great opportunity, and I'd love to fill the position, but if you can't wait two weeks for me to give proper notice and spend time with my mother after my father just died, then this isn't the kind of company I want to work for. I hope you'll reconsider." I stood up and he scrambled out of his seat completely nonplussed. I shook his hand. "It was nice meeting you," I said, cursing myself silently for being so stupid.

I got the job.

And started after Christmas.

But honestly, if it weren't for all those other setbacks I wouldn't have pushed myself so hard to learn the business and have the confidence to know that I didn't have to sacrifice my morals for a job, which ultimately landed me my dream job in the end.

Setbacks make you stronger. And when you finally do reach your destination, the victory tastes so much sweeter.

"Truce," says Henri when he comes home from work and we're both quiet. I'm still mad he won't co-sign for me to get some money from my 401k. We put on a show for the kids that there's no tension between us. When the kids are asleep he pours himself a cocktail. I would have one too, but I'm only a few weeks out so I mix up my protein shake.

I wish I could drink alcohol.

I wish I could crunch on chips.

I wish I could soothe myself with chocolate.

But since comfort food is no longer an option I suppose I'll just have to comfort myself directly and try to break this impasse between us.

"Can we talk?" I ask tentatively.

"Here's one thousand dollars."

My eyes open wide. He places a white envelope in my hand.

"Use it for your training, your posing classes, your bikinis, your supplements, your whatever. But I don't want to hear another word about this competition."

I place the envelope down on the coffee table and look at him.

"This isn't working," I say.

"What's not working?"

"I don't want to keep asking you for money. This isn't working for me. I feel like a child. I don't do the same amount of work as you on the building, but I do work. I do the bookkeeping and lease files and government filings, and raise the kids, and that's not nothing. If I didn't do it, we would have to pay someone else to do it for us."

"Now you want to hire a bookkeeper?"

"No, I want to get some of my own money again. And then I want to be a bigger part of the business. I don't want you to feel like I'm useless."

"I never said that."

"Well, that's how I feel."

"You're raising the kids. That's important to you, and I see it's good for them. I want to make all your dreams come true. I just can't do everything."

"Then let me help you. How about after this show I'll take a month off from training and work at the building. I feel so much better when I'm working, Henri."

"I thought you wanted to be a stay-at-home-mom?"

"I do. But Henry starts nursery school part-time in the fall, and I'd love to take a more active role in the business. You know, I do have thirteen years experience in real estate."

"I know." We are now facing each other on the couch. Our bodies mirror each other.

"So let me work with you. Team Traugott, remember?" I quirk a smile, which he shadows back to me.

"Fair enough. Look, Lisa, I know you love this bodybuilding thing. I understand why; I used to love it myself.Can we just make it through this first competition?" He runs his hand through his hair.

"Done," I say.

"And don't bring up shit from the past in the middle of an argument. I hate when you do that."

"It's the history major in me. Sorry." I reach for him and we hug tightly.

"I'm sorry," we say in unison.

METROFLEX

I drive to Metroflex and park near the door. It's a giant warehouse, and the parking lot is broken asphalt and gravel mixed with dry cracked dirt. I open the glass door and walk inside. A man with blond hair is behind the reception desk, talking on the phone. I look at the wall behind me. It has pictures of bodybuilders onstage holding trophies. The pictures are framed and signed.

I tell the man that I'm Daniel's client and he smiles and has me fill out some paperwork. He says the membership is on autopay with my credit card (a relief that they at least have that) and I'll pay Daniel directly for training.

I'm here early, so I look around after I finish the paperwork. There is an area on the other side of the reception area where they sell men's T-shirts and supplements. There are a few tank tops for women.

There are two individual bathrooms. The women's bathroom has a poster of a woman looking hot and strong lifting weights and a photocopied advertisement for spray on tan. I move to the kitchen area. On the other side is the gym. Rap music is blaring on the other side, but I stay where I'm at.

A large conference table is in the middle, surrounded by mismatched office chairs. There is a sticker on the table of a bodybuilder next to a weight kneeling beneath a cross and it says "True Power." The walls are covered in pictures of Phil Heath, Kai Greene and Branch Warren doing poses, and women with six-pack stomachs from pages ripped out from magazines. The latest NPC winners are taped to the walls and I look at them, wondering what it feels like to win.

"You can go in," the man says to me.

I open the door and the music is so loud I can feel the vibrations. There is a picnic table with keys and Tupperware containers on it. A handful of people are working out.

Daniel is with a client, but he smiles at me.

"Go warm up." He nods in the general direction of some StairMasters and treadmills. I climb on the stepper. It's so rickety compared to the equipment at 24 Hour Fitness. Also, everything is damp from the moisture in the air.

The sides of the warehouse have metal gates that are open. I can see that outside a trainer has his client running with a rope around his waist. Then I see a giant tire attached to the rope. It's not like a regular tire either; it's a tire from a tractor or something 'cause it's huge.

There is a man who has almost like a Mohawk hairstyle with bleach blond hair and he's more muscular than anyone I've ever met in my entire life. He is using the cable machine and has it on full weights. Two other men are lifting with him in rotation and they are almost as large. One is struggling and Mohawk man says, "Come on, bitch!" and the other man grunts through it.

A few women are doing chin ups with a woman trainer. They are laughing between sets.

I am so out of my league.

Daniel is with his client, some man in his 40s maybe? The man is doing sit-ups on the incline bench as Daniel tosses a medicine ball to him.

I feel bad for sending him that bitchy text the other day. I feel even worse about the uneasy truce between Henri and me. I now have the money for the last month of training, but at what cost? Is Henri going to add this to his apparently lengthy list of things he's mad at me for?

Daniel nods his head for me to come over. "Everything OK?" he asks. His eyebrows scrunch in a little bit.

"I'm sorry about the other day. The text message, I mean," I say rather sheepishly.

"I just have to be fair to—"

"I know," I cut him off. "The text really had nothing to do with you. Henri and I just had the mother of all fights about money and that's when I read your text."

"Oh . . . everything OK?"

"Yup," I say flatly. "Here's your money. Let's do an Operation Ass Lift."

"What do you mean?"

"All of the women who won had these cute little bubble butts, so I need to work on that. Just tell me what to do and I'll do it."

"That won't happen before this show, Lisa."

"Why not?"

"I'm not a miracle worker."

We are doing legs today. Good. The more weight the better. I've got residual anger and nothing gets it out like the leg press. I don't even care if he kills me with the workout.

After training, I go home and shower. Then, after Henri leaves for work, and Rylee for school, I take Little Henry with me and do something I should have done a long time ago. I open my own checking account again.

The upside of being the CEO of the family business is that I don't need anyone's signature beyond my own to make financial decisions. It wasn't much, just $150 a week dividends on autopay from the business account to my own, but it's enough to pay for my training costs and the occasional cup of coffee or new jeans without dispute or explanation.

I've earned it.

HAPPY 25 X 2

If you are my trainer, I'm totally cool with you reading this post. Even though it describes my sheer bliss over eating ice cream cake a few days ago. Know why you can read it? Because you approved it!

Yes, mark your calendar folks, Daniel let me eat crap 5-1/2 weeks before my show. How did this craziness come about? Well, I was at Walmart (of course) getting birthday cake for Henri and even though I already knew the answer, I felt it was worth the attempt to ask for ice cream cake. Allow me to share my text messages with you . . .

> **Lisa**: On a scale of 1-10, 1 meaning no problem and 10 meaning hell no, what r my chances of eating a slice of ice cream cake tonite for Henri's 50th birthday?
> **Daniel**: U know the answer to that
> **Lisa**: Ah man . . . fine. I'll eat protein pudding.
> **Daniel**: You're 5 weeks, right?

OMG, is he actually considering this????

> **Lisa**: 5-1/2 weeks.

That extra 1/2 week makes all the difference in the world right? 'Cause it's more like 7 or 10 weeks out.

> **Daniel**: Okay. How much u weigh?

This could be a trick question. I'm not supposed to weigh myself, but f*** it, I want ice cream cake.

> **Lisa**: 111
> **Daniel**: What kinda cake?
> **Lisa**: Carvel ice cream cake
> **Daniel**: And can you stick to one piece?
> **Lisa**: Yes, yes, yes!
> **Daniel**: Okay one small piece and this is your cheat meal before your reunion.

Seriously???? Daniel????? Did I text the wrong trainer?

> **Lisa**: YAHOO!!!!!!!!!!! THANK U!!!!
> **Daniel**: One small piece.

Did you notice he felt the need to repeat that?

Lisa: Promise
Daniel: Don't eat it past 7 pm and don't have any carbs and I'd prefer it be after u workout
Lisa: Done

I will agree to any oddball rules if it means I can eat cake.

Daniel: If u can, just enjoy
Lisa: :☺
Daniel: No more. Got it?

Guess he didn't believe my "promise."

Lisa: Yes! I promise I will only have 1 small piece after I workout ☺
Daniel: Perfect . . . Have a protein shake after as well.
Lisa: Will do. YAY!
Daniel: After that u have to stay on track.

So then I called Henri speaking so fast I barely made sense. "YouhavetocomehomefromworkontimesoIcangetaworkoutinandthenbedones oIcanhavecakebecauseithastobeaftertheworkoutbutbefore7pmsocomehomen owok?"

He's been dealing with crazy things like this for a while now—we've been married 8 years— so he just went with it, and we all had a good time. And I even made him younger! (I wrote Happy 25 x 2 on his birthday cake.) He doesn't know this yet, but I'm throwing him a big surprise birthday party in California after my competition. After the past few years of hardship, a celebration is due. He's earned it.

OPERATION ASS LIFT

The women who won the fitness competitions all had at least one thing in common: bootylicious backsides. I want one. And since I'm not a gazillionaire who can purchase one via plastic surgery, I guess I'll be doing lots of squats.

I have persisted in annoying Daniel about Operation Ass Lift all week until he gave me a concrete exercise plan to address this, because I refuse to accept, "I'm not a miracle worker" as an answer. That's an excuse! *Ha, ha, Daniel, bet you never thought that I'd throw that back at ya!*

I didn't realize that growing muscle takes longer than losing fat, so I understand that I won't have a cute little bubble butt for this show, but I will get one some day.

He told me to do 400 lunges per day, 5 days per week with a 40 lb. bar on my back. If that doesn't lift my ass by the end of the year I will cry.

DSST: Can I Binge Drink at My Reunion?

It's now time for another episode of Dumb Shit I Said to My Trainer . . .

We are at Metroflex Gym and it's crazy hot. Like just-stand-still-and-sweat hot. But I'm sweating for a different reason.

Asking your trainer for permission to go off your diet is like asking your dad for the keys to the car. You pretty much know the answer is going to be no, but you have to ask it anyway. Heck, he let me eat ice cream cake; it's worth a shot.

I'm doing chest presses on the rickety old equipment. A woman trainer—Mel?—is standing with a group of women by the squat rack. I watch them do a set and then crowd around her to giggle at something on her cell phone. A big dude with a heavy chain over his shoulders hops up the wooden stairs balanced on one leg while some scary looking trainer with piercings, tattoos and a goatee is flipping through text messages while his client grunts in pain.

"Guess what?"

"What?"

"I'm at My Buffy Weight! One hundred seven!" I am beaming. He gives me a high five.

"That's great!" I think he is almost as happy as I am, because now he doesn't have to hear about "My Buffy Weight" any more. I guess I'll have to name my new weight "My 1st Show Weight," whatever that will be. I say 1st show because I intend on doing another one, and another, and another after that. I will bodybuild until they kick me off the stage.

"So your reunion is coming up soon. Do you have a plan?"

"Plan?"

"You're going to be gone for four days. Do you know where you're going to work out?"

"24 Hour Fitness," I said without missing a beat. *I hadn't thought at all about exercise.*

"There's one near your mom's?"

"Uh huh." *I have no idea. But it's 24 Hour Fitness. They're like the Starbucks of gyms; they're everywhere.*

"And your food?"

"I emailed my mom my meal plan." *That I actually did.*

"Good. Are you excited?" asked Daniel as I pressed away.

"Yeah. Well, excited and nervous."

"Nervous? Why? You look great. Everyone else will be balding or fat."

"I guess. So . . . about the reunion. Can I have a cheater's *weekend?*" Only when I said "weekend" it sounded like it came out of my five-year-old's mouth because it was like eight octaves higher than normal.

"No. I just gave you ice cream cake so you won't cheat at your reunion! No. You'll be too close to your show. You just made your Buffy Weight! You're a month out, Lisa!"

"Well how about a cheat *meal* then?"

"We'll see."

We'll see? This was unexpected news! Quick! Ride the wave of generosity!

"And wine?"

Uh oh. He gave me the look. I just pushed too far.

"No, Lisa. We've been through this before. You know you can't drink alcohol so close to the show. And I thought you said you don't even really like alcohol." He loads more plates and it becomes a struggle for me to lift.

"I don't. But. IT'S MY TWENTIETH HIGH SCHOOL REUNION! Ima need a drink."

"Really?" he asks in a way that tells me he thinks I'm being totally lame.

"I'll call you before your twentieth high school reunion and see how sober you'll be. How about vodka?"

"No."

"One shot?"

"No."

I sulk quietly as I lift the weights. *He'll be one of those dads who never lets his kids drive the car.* But then suddenly a brilliant idea enters my head and I let go of the bar. It flings in the air and the weights drop with such a heavy crash Daniel jumps back and everyone in the gym stops and looks.

"WHAT IF I PROMISE TO THROW UP AFTERWARDS!?!" I ask triumphantly.

After he gets up (he fell over laughing at me) . . . he said no.

The end.

JERSEY GIRL

I'm a Jersey Girl and my thoughts are headed home as we board the plane to my mom's house. When people hear New Jersey, it usually is at the end of a punch line, or they think of Snooki or the Jersey accent; but it's my home and I miss it sometimes.

Coming of age in Jersey meant you dated one of the three I's: Italy, Israel or Ireland. Sometimes you'd get really lucky and date a combo like a Jewish-Italian guy. These cultures also had a strong impact on the local cuisine.

Every fall I crave matzo ball soup and potato latkes, but it's a rather specific craving. I don't like the matzo ball soup with the noodles in it, just the one with the giant matzo ball that fills the entire cup with a few slices of carrot in it. And I take my latkes with sour cream and applesauce on the side. And, of course, what is life without a bagel? Oy vey!

But then I start thinking about other Jersey foods. The only real Irish food I miss is beer. Throw a stone in Jersey and you will hit some Irish pub named O'something complete with a blue-eyed Irish lad full of very funny, very dirty jokes.

I miss that part of it too. The witty in-your-face banter that is totally acceptable. California, where I lived for the bulk of my 20s and 30s, is very PC and people only spoke about surfing, or clothes, or maybe real estate in the beach bars. I tried to have a discussion about the Iraq War back in 2002 and people looked at me like I was crazy.

Texans seem to appreciate the Jersey sense of humor more, but sometimes I feel like I don't fit in here either. I curse too much, struggle with my faith, and am a Democrat. Or, to use a Texan saying, "I'm as welcome here as a skunk at a lawn party."

My favorite Jersey boys are Jon Stewart and Chris Christie. I know, I know, I'm a Democrat, why do I like Chris Christie? Because even though I completely disagree with his politics, he has great smart-ass comebacks. Example: At some town hall meeting, Mitt Romney was speaking and people in the back started booing and saying, "Romney is a job killer!" Romney said something like, "Now, now, settle down, please." Chris Christie started speaking and the same people called out, "Christie is a job killer!" and without batting an eye he said, "Something might be going down tonight, sweetheart, but it ain't jobs." **OH SNAP!**

And then, my favorite, the Italian influence. The pizza is different in New York and New Jersey. Jersey peeps don't use a fork for pizza! The crust is hard on the bottom and you fold it in half until it cracks, and then you let all the grease drip down on your paper plate. It sounds disgusting, I know, but trust me it's the best pizza you'll find anywhere on the planet.

Trenton (pronounced Tren-in) has a Little Italy filled with awesome restaurants, and you can smell the tomatoes and mozzarella from your car as you get closer. Lasagna, fettuccine alfredo, Italian cheesecake, oh I could go on forever!

But my competition is in 5 weeks, so I'm not supposed to eat any of that. And it makes me sad, because I'm realizing how much "home" is defined by food; right or wrong it is. Hmm. Maybe I'll figure out a way to ship some of it back to Austin. Or maybe I'll just cheat?

PARTY LIKE IT'S 1992!

The year 1992 doesn't seem so long ago to me, and yet here I stand at my 20th high school reunion.

Biggest change over the last 20 years? The Jersey perms went away.

We all have to wear name tags with our senior year pictures and, no kidding, EVERY single woman had that same perm in high school. But overall, my class KICKED ASS! Pediatric surgeons, small business owners, CFOs, publicists . . . heck, there is even a gym-owning bodybuilder dude in the mix who lives in Florida now.

We ask each other about the missing people.

"What's Carole up to?"

"She's a science teacher with two kids."

"And Nicole?"

"She's a paralegal with a son and twins."

"Hey, is Janet here? She used to be a total _____"

Hey! Ho! Hip hop hurray! Ho! blares the '90s music. It's like being on the treadmill at 24 Hour Fitness and listening to my iPod.

So many women are pregnant!

"We have a nine-year-old, a seven-year-old and an oops! due in a few months."

Some people look almost exactly the same (minus the perm) and others seemed to have changed form completely.

The bar was open all night and *in vino veritas*, especially when you are holding a glass of wine in each hand.

"I had such a crush on your wife in school. You're a lucky man," the boy from religion class tells my husband.

"Yes, I am," smiles Henri.

Spying the boy from English Lit, I confess, giggling, "I had such a crush on you."

"I'm gay," he says.

"Yes, clearly," I laugh, "But I didn't know that when I was fourteen."

A break in the music and then, *I'm too sexy for my shirt, so sexy it hurts* . . .

But I'm not too sexy for that pasta! Hot damn, I miss Italian food! But, apparently, things have changed, even in New Jersey.

"I read your 'Jersey Girl' post. Wow, you really haven't been here for a while. Little Italy is now Little Puerto Rico."

"Really?"

"Si."

I worked my way through the crowd.

"I've been in pharmaceuticals for fourteen years."

"I've been in my father's business since after school."

Some classmates went to Boston, others Baltimore and D.C. Some worked in Philly, others New York, but most stayed close to home in Jersey.

"I live in Robbinsville."

"I live in Ewing."

"I live in Bordentown, and you?"

"Well . . . first I was an actress living in New York City, and did two national tours playing Anne Frank and Scout in *To Kill A Mockingbird*, then moved to Los Angeles and was on *Buffy the Vampire Slayer*, got my real estate license, managed a forty-eight-story high rise, got married, moved to San Diego, had two kids, moved to Austin, Texas, where we own a twenty-seven-unit apartment building and flip houses now, gained weight, started bodybuilding, lost weight and now I blog about it all."

"WAIT, WHAT???"

Jump around! Jump around! Jump up, jump up and get down! Jump! Jump! Jump!

The dance floor got packed again. If nothing else, leading a crazy life was worth it just to see the shocked expressions reflected in my classmates' ever-widening eyes.

My husband met my ex-boyfriend.

That was weird.

Equally weird is that a bunch of people from my high school are following my blog so they are congratulating me on the weight loss, and talking to Henri like they knew him forever. Not a ton of people are following me—maybe 400 on the blog and almost 100 on the Facebook page, but when you are followed by people who you actually know and run into from time to time, you kind of feel famous. Totally weird, huh?

But not as weird as the next conversation.

"Remember when I dumped you?" asked Tim.

"Wait, what? I thought it was mutual." *See, deep down subconsciously I knew there was a reason why I would need to drink.*

"No. I dumped you, remember? And everyone was mad at me about it?"

"I guess somewhere over the course of time I forgot that part . . . well . . . guess you're regretting that now—I look pretty hot!"

Most everyone had kids and a spouse, and I was particularly proud of mine. My 20-year course was anything but linear, and I'm happy to have traveled a long part of that bumpy road with Henri. We've built a great life together.

My classmates seem genuinely happy with their life choices too. An interesting life is doubly sweet, I've heard it told: once when you live it and again when you retell it.

May your life be twice sweet as well.

SELF-SABOTAGE—PART 2

After returning to Texas, reality sunk in. I had gone to New Jersey and my reunion with the best of intentions, but obviously those intentions didn't give a crap. It was time to pay the piper.

We returned on Monday afternoon and the next morning I had a training session at 10 a.m., so that gave me a little time to self-correct. I ate clean from the moment the plane landed in Texas. I went to the gym Monday night with my arctic sweat gear on and did cardio for about an hour, followed by the sauna for 15 minutes. My friend at the 24 reception desk asked, "Did you cheat on your diet? All the blog posts before your reunion mentioned food but the post about the reunion didn't mention anything about food at all."

"Oh, you noticed that omission?"

"Yeah . . . I'm sorry, don't think I'm stalking you."

I laughed out loud, "I started the blog in part to keep myself accountable, so it's working. I totally cheated and I'm trying to work it off before tomorrow."

Tuesday morning I was up at 3:30 a.m. Henri looked at me getting my sweats on.

"I love you, but you're nuts," he said, rolling over and promptly snoring.

I got to the gym and did my cardio and then the sauna, and psyched myself up to see Daniel later at Metroflex.

When I arrive at Metroflex I have a thousand things on my mind. I get on the stepper to warm up while Daniel finishes with his client. Music is blaring. The thermometer on the wall says 98 degrees.

His client is finishing with overhead presses in front of the mirror. They both laugh at something and give each other a high five upon departure. He nods me over and I descend, carrying my water bottle with me.

Today is shoulder/chest day and I start to tug on my gloves.

"I read your blog post about your reunion. It looks like you had fun."

"Uh huh."

"Did you get compliments for your weight loss?"

"Uh huh."

He doesn't comment on how I look. Good! He doesn't notice the weight gain! It also helps that I'm wearing a loose T-shirt instead of my usual tank top to hide the belly flab.

"How are your abs?"

Oh shit. "They're gone," I say not looking at him. The first place I gain weight is my stomach, so my muscle tone is now completely hidden.

"Gone?"

I lift my shirt to my belly button.

"I cheated on my diet," I mumble, avoiding his gaze.

"I was afraid that would happen. I gave you an ice cream cake cheat last week so you wouldn't do this." I say nothing. "Was it one meal? A few?"

"All weekend. You don't want to know, you'll just get mad."

"Tell me," he says quietly.

I confess it all, and he doesn't say anything for a minute. The funny thing is that I almost want him to yell at me, like he did that other client, because I just feel so awful. I feel like a drug addict in relapse.

"I'm not going to call you out; I see you feel bad. What's done is done. At least it happened four weeks out and not the week before the show. You're going to have to do sixty minutes of cardio for the next six days, eat clean, and hope that you come in right for the show."

I feel so bad, like I disappointed my coach. I shift my weight from leg to leg, wanting to start the workout. Instead of moving to the equipment, though, he sits on the wooden top of the picnic table, Metroflex's hardcore version of a locker room. Everyone just throws their keys and gym bags there.

"Hey, let's just talk for a minute."

No. I don't want to talk. I don't want another "pep talk." I want to just forget about what happened in New Jersey and move on to my workout.

"Everyone messes up, you know." His voice is quiet but steady, and I strain to hear him over the music. I don't want to talk. But then he doesn't talk about my binge last weekend at all. He tells me about one of his own personal failures—what happened and why he thinks he messed up so bad.

We've spoken to each other about stuff going on in our lives before, but this was the first time he ever seemed ashamed—vulnerable. I try to make a joke, because that's what I always do in uncomfortable situations, but he doesn't laugh.

"No. I messed up and screwed myself over in the process. It was a really humbling experience for me." He looks away from me, watching people climbing on the StairMaster. "Lisa, you're an emotional eater. Whenever you go to your parents' home there are all sorts of triggers. Your family—they don't understand what the hell bodybuilding is. They think you look great, so it's OK to eat whatever, and you fall back into old patterns. But you're back now, and I don't want to see you throw everything away that you've worked so hard for. Think where you were when we met. I'm so proud of you, and what you've done in four months."

His words kind of hang in the air.

"You're a good trainer," I say.

"Come on." He moves to the chest flye machine. It's wobbly and I find it difficult to keep my form. I'm still quiet. "What?" he asks.

"Do you think I'm going to gain all the weight back?" There. I said it out loud, my biggest fear.

"No," he said without hesitation. "Not after you worked so hard. Shit, not after *I* worked so hard; I won't *let* you gain it back."

We both laugh and then I said, "Someone I know said, 'I bet she gains it all back after the reunion.'"

He shakes his head slowly, exhaling through his nose in annoyance. "Sometimes you females can be so cruel to each other. Some women are like that. It probably had more to do with her, and what was going on in her life, than you. People are going to say things. Just let it go."

I continue with my next set.

"Look at that girl on the treadmill. How does she look to you?"

"I don't know. Overweight. Like how I looked two months ago."

"She won a competition last year."

"Really?"

"Yeah, really."

"Well what happened?"

"She went crazy in the off-season, thinking she could just eat whatever she wanted. It's not like that, Lisa. This is a *lifestyle*. To grow lean muscle mass you do *clean* bulking. You add more carbs into your diet, not just eat cheeseburgers from McDonald's. That doesn't get you anything other than more work you have to do for the next show. You don't want that do you?"

"No." I finish my last rep.

"Rest. For your show weight you will probably get down to one hundred pounds—"

"One hundred pounds?! Really!?!" I interrupt.

"Relax. You'll be one hundred pounds for your show weight, and then it's the off-season and you'll be working on gaining lean muscle mass. You'll be between one hundred fourteen and one hundred twenty pounds."

"But I don't want to be one hundred twenty pounds. I want to stay one hundred pounds."

"No one stays their show weight beyond the show, that's why in all the muscle magazines it lists their show weight and off-season weight. Make sense?"

"Yeah, probably. I don't know."

"Lisa, you're not going to get fat again; stop listening to other people. You're reshaping your body. A muscular size three looks a lot better than just a skinny size one, trust me."

"OK . . . so I guess I'm going to have to keep doing competitions just to prove her wrong, stay in shape forever, and piss her off."

He smirks. "Bodybuilding's addictive, huh?" He has me move to the bench to do skull crushers. I'm lying on the bench holding a 15 lb. dumbbell over my head and bending at the elbows to drop the weight back over my forehead.

"Yeah, I love it. Hey, did you ever hit yourself doing this?"

"I think once, maybe, when I was tired?"

I get an image of him knocking himself out in the middle of 24 Hour Fitness and start laughing. "You know, that's why people think bodybuilders are dumb. Because they see these big guys in the gym hitting their own heads with dumbbells." I'm laughing so hard I have to put the weight down.

"Yes, we're all dumb," he says condescendingly.

I sit up. "Before I started doing this I thought bodybuilders were all like Hanz and Franz."

"Do you get all your information from late night sketch comedies?" He hands me the weight and I get back to lifting.

"I don't know; does Jon Stewart really qualify as 'late night'? I think he's more along the lines of 'early evening' sketch comedy."

He's counting the reps. "Three, four, watch your form. Do you still think that bodybuilders are dumb?"

"Of course not. I had no idea what a mental game this was."

"Seven, eight, good. Rest."

"I had no idea how much science was involved: timing of meals and macronutrients, protein and muscle growth—"

"Everyone thinks you need steroids to grow muscle. You just need to know about food. It's crazy isn't it?" He hands me a 20 lb. weight. "Go again."

"And I thought that all the women would be just like they were in *Mean Girls*." I pause for a moment. "I really do get all my information from sketch comedies."

"It's not like that though, is it?"

"No. Everyone in the posing class has been so nice to me. And people you'd never expect to enter bikini competitions are doing it—moms with four kids, and third grade teachers, and people who've survived cancer. Not what I expected at all."

"Everyone has a story if you listen to them."

He takes the weight and we continue the workout. He tells me what to expect this last month. He gives me my new diet. Yay! He put me back on fat burners again. My diet's going to change again in a week. Double yay!! He explains we're in a maintenance phase now. I'll be too tired and carb-depleted to make any real muscle gains. He's worried I might come in too thin, but says he'd rather have me look too hard versus too soft. I'm getting psyched. I'm excited to be coming down the homestretch.

"I have something else to tell you," he says.

"What?"

"I'm moving back to Houston at the end of the month."

Shit.

SHE'S LOSING IT

In the book *Ninety Days: A Memoir of Recovery* the author, Bill Clegg, writes about the all encompassing thoughts that filled his head when he wanted to get high, the complete suspension of considering consequences as he cashed out his credit cards and rent money to pay for his fix, and the self-abhorrence that followed his benders.

While I'm happy to say I've been lucky enough to avoid drug addiction (I just said no), the other day I began to consider that perhaps I had a teensy, tiny (OK, huge, colossal) issue with food.

I thought Cheater's Weekend had cured my food "addiction" but, as I discovered in New Jersey, I'm one long weekend away from catastrophe. I'm not maxing out my credit cards for crack, but I'm certainly not thinking like a sane human being either . . .

It's 5:30 a.m. Henri and the kids are sleeping and it's quiet and dark outside. I put on my sneakers to do cardio penance and skip the gym entirely. I just run through the silent streets, past the sleeping houses and lights that line their path. A cop car drives by and I wave. The sun will be rising within the hour.

I think about what went wrong in New Jersey and come up with quite a few things. The most important reason why I went offtrack was because I wanted to. The instant gratification of food before me right now was more important than the delayed gratification of looking good in a bikini four weeks from now.

I wanted to have a taste of home, and salad wasn't going to cut it. I also felt deprived from following such a strict meal plan for so many months. Even though I cheated on it from time to time, for the most part I really did follow the plan, and I was now wearing the size 3 jeans to prove it. Daniel, my outsourced willpower, was out of town and, let's face it, sometimes it's just plain fun to rebel when you know you won't get caught immediately. Those were the easy reasons. Then things got more complicated.

It would have felt weird to not eat what my mother put on the table. I didn't want to feel left out in my own home. I was so thin, what would one weekend of binge eating matter?

Then there was the reunion. Alcohol to calm my nerves, and make me not so shy. Even though I knew these people, why were those illogical feelings popping up? And then my weird fear of success. Would the women not like me if I'm in shape and they're not? Would the men pay too much attention? But my fears, of course, proved false. People at the reunion were supportive and friendly, just like they were in high school, actually.

Then there was the incident. The really bad one that happened while I was in college and only 20 years old. The one that made me fear betrayal from women and skewed my perception of how men paid attention to me and my body. We are all guided in part by a map of our hurts. My map told me, "Don't be the best you can be. Women will try to destroy you. Men will try to overpower you." That one incident, ultimately, created my trust issues, and my map guided me to food to protect myself.

I run through the center of town. Past the fire station and little shops. A restaurant is illuminated and the strong scent of bacon is in the air. My mouth waters, but I keep running. Past the gas station and the flower shop. The sky is turning pink and the stars are getting dimmer.

It's time for me to let go of the past and just push through it. All these emotions that I buried for so long are out, and now that I'm looking at them, I can finally get some closure. What happened to me happened almost 20 years ago. One event is no longer going to retain so much power over me.

I'm not going to hide my body anymore. I'm not going to let memories make me feel awkward about my sexuality or feel like I have to make myself less to fit in for the rest of my life.

I'm running along a creek now and the sun begins to rise. Faster and faster I run.

I'm losing it.

I'm losing the weight.

I'm losing the excuses, self-sabotage, and worrying over what everybody thinks.

I'm losing the starving myself and binging, and the feelings of guilt and self-loathing after.

I'm at the top of the hill now and my arms rise above my head, because in losing everything,

I just won back myself.

IF YOU CAN'T TONE IT, TAN IT

Perhaps the weirdest aspect of the bodybuilding sport (next to posing, of course) is the whole tanning thing. The most basic question is: *why do they do this?*

Answer:
1. To show more muscle striations and definition
2. To counter the harsh stage lights that wash everything out (think of actors wearing "stage" makeup)

There are two tanning processes to go through. The first is getting a base tan. The second, more odd process apparently, is the spray-on tan and oil coat right before the show.

A base tan is helpful if you are extremely pale (like me). If you live somewhere sunny and warm and have an hour or so to spare, put on your bathing suit and enjoy. If you are time pressed or reside in a climate-challenged locale, a tanning salon is your other option.

This is the first time I ever used a tanning bed. Here is an excerpt of my conversation:

Lisa: So how does this work? Do I wear a bathing suit?
Tanning salon lady: Well, most people don't want tan lines, so they do it in the nude.
Lisa: *Ohhhhh* . . . How long do I go in for? Like thirty minutes?
Tanning salon lady: You're pretty pale. How about five minutes?
Lisa: I'll try for seven minutes.

I was paying for 30 minutes after all . . .

She shows me the different bronzers, all super-duper expensive ($65 per bottle) and I was directed to room 8. Room 8 has country music playing. Apparently, each room has its own soundtrack. I strip down and start applying the lotion. It feels pretty nice on my pasty white skin.

A little brown towel is on the chair to wipe the bronzer off my palms, lest they turn orange. On top of the towel there are little goofy eyeball things to put over my eyes, but they don't seem to want to stay in my eye sockets.

It's a good thing I'm not claustrophobic because when I go into the tanning bed I have to close it over myself, as if I'm a vampire in a coffin. Suddenly the bed starts beeping at me. *Oh s***! What did I do wrong?* Lights and heat lamps go on in a blinding glare. Game on.

There are buttons in the top right corner that control different things so I press the fan blower button just to check it out. A fan kicked on and one of those goofy eyeball things falls off my face and manages to roll under the machine. *Oh great.*

But since I only have a limited time frame, I can't worry about finding the singular goggle. I just close my eyes and enjoy the warmth. It feels *divine*.

Beep! My seven moments in the (fake) sun are over, and I look in the mirror. Now, I want you to think of the most embarrassing spots you could possibly sunburn yourself . . . that's where I just burned myself. Not to brag, but I also burned my armpits too. That's pretty impressive for just seven minutes.

Another fun thing I notice is that while my front half and back half are tannish-pink, my sides are completely white because that's where my arms rested. It seems you are supposed to rotate like a rotisserie chicken during this process to prevent that.

Oh well. *I'll know for next time!*

DSST: Toast?

It's now time for another episode of Dumb Shit I Said to My Trainer . . .

It's 8:50 p.m. and Henri and I are watching TV. Henri is eating the tacos I made him and I am getting taco envy. Honestly, I'm getting any-kind-of-food envy these days. I've been eating my last carbs for the day by noon because it's so hard to spread my food out every three hours like I'm supposed to, and I devoured my casein protein shake over an hour ago.

Anyway, Henri's eating his tacos, which he loaded up with cheddar cheese, and they smell overwhelmingly good to me.

"I want a taco."

"You can't have one, you're three weeks out. Suck it up, soldier." He takes an extra big bite.

Sometimes I don't like Henri very much.

"I'm hungry. I'm going to ask Daniel if I can eat something."

"He's not going to let you eat a taco!"

"Well, *duh*, I'm not going to ask him that!" *Really, Henri.*

"Stop asking him dumb shit when you know he's just going to say no," he laughed, taking a sip of his Pepsi.

I want Pepsi . . .

"Sometimes he surprises me. He let me have ice cream cake a few weeks ago, after all." I'm so hungry I could chew off my arm. I send Daniel a text.

8:52 p.m. Lisa: I'm starving. Can I have a piece of Ezekiel toast?
8:53 p.m. Daniel: No

"Damn."

"Told you," Henri says.

I hate them both.

FOOD DREAMS #2

Have you ever had Hostess apple pies? Well two nights ago I had a dream that I was at the Wawa in New Jersey (of course a dream involving forbidden fruit pie is set in Jersey. . .) and I bought one of those pies, only instead of it being about 4 inches it was 24 inches, and after I bit into it I read the calorie count that said it was 500 calories per bite, and I didn't know how I would ever fit into my bikini in time for the show. I sat up in bed thoroughly confused and not sure if I had eaten a pie or not. Ah, stress dreams.

But you know what? I burned off the binge and I'm back to My Buffy Weight. *Whew!*

Also, my bikinis arrived! Henri helped me find two on E-Bay; a green one and a sparkly blue one. I showed both to Adela and she said to go with the sparkles. I love bodybuilding!

THIS IS A TEST

You have three weeks to go before show day and you are invited to a party at Dave and Lucrecia's high-rise overlooking Lady Bird Lake. This is the same couple your trainer would refer to as a "bad influence" with respect to clean eating. The food placed in front of you looks fantastically good and smells even better, causing your mouth to salivate like Pavlov's dogs.

Do you:

a) Demonstrate complete control, drinking only bottled water, and earn a much deserved golf clap from the party's attendees?

b) Behave like a reasonable adult, sticking to the grilled chicken and roasted vegetables, singing "la, la, la, la, la" in your head to block out Daniel's voice, which is saying, "You don't know how they made that chicken . . ."?

c) Go just a teensy-weensy overboard, just a little bit, eating the above-mentioned healthy choices plus a ~~few~~ (OK—a plate) of crackers with high-end cheese and ~~one~~ (OK—four Diet Cokes), knowing that you can do cardio penance for the next 20 days?

d)   Party like it's last week in New Jersey?

What would you do? *Guess what I did?*

Ha! Ha! Well, you're wrong! 'Cause I only drank water at the party!!! Go me!

THE TIGRESS IS SLEEPING

I used to be a Tiger Mom. I earned this title even before the book was written by Amy Chua. My oldest child, Rylee Brianna, bore the brunt of this. My husband and I were the crazy competitive couple at Gymboree class. Rylee did her part by being the first kid to roll over, the first to stand, the first to crawl and the first to walk in the class. But she was not the first to sit up. That was Hailey.

The babies were on their little baby bellies rolling balls across a mirror while the parents sang, "Twinkle, Twinkle, Little Star." Rylee, as usual, rolled over and everyone *oohed* and *ahhhed* and then little Hailey sat up. She sat up! And she was 11 days younger than Rylee! How could this happen?!

Henri and I looked at each other. Our eyes narrowed.

"Bring it on, Hailey."

I was still working after I had Rylee to keep our medical insurance (and, let's face it, living in California is expensive), so the time I did spend with her was . . . well . . . intense. It also didn't help that my husband worked from home, so he got to be the fun stay-at-home-dad while I had to deal with office politics and mother's guilt.

We went to Babies "R" Us and bought a pink Bumbo to help Rylee strengthen her back muscles so she could sit on her own. I also purchased the complete set of *Your Baby Can Read!* by Dr. Robert Titzer and showed her the word flash cards while she sat in the Bumbo to make sure she spent enough time in the contraption. (I had to make this purchase in a stealth manner as Henri thought I was crazy for even attempting this baby phonics project.)

Needless to say, Rylee was not only sitting at the next Gymboree class but also could read the words "hi" and "clap."

When Little Henry was born I very happily quit my job and moved to Austin, Texas. I kept up the Tiger Mom thing pretty well . . . at first. At the age of 2-1/2, Rylee was reading Level 1 reader books, counting to 100, and knew quite a few words in Spanish.

I bought a blue Bumbo in preparation for Little Henry and started him with the *Baby Can Read* videos while I fed him organic green beans I pureed in my Magic Bullet blender. But something happened on the way to Harvard prep nursery school. . . .

My son wanted no part of the Tiger Mom thing. Rylee was focused, and she did everything I asked of her with enthusiasm. Henry wanted to sleep and cuddle. I put Henry in the Bumbo and he found a way to slide out of it. I showed him a flash card and he wanted to use it as a teething biscuit.

Rylee crawled at 6 months and walked at 9 months. Henry was 8 months old and still was content to sit in his bouncer and observe. I enlisted Rylee's help. We both got on our hands and knees and demonstrated crawling techniques for him. He just laughed a little mocking baby laugh.

A week later there was a drum out of his reach, so he got up and walked to it.

From that point on he was into everything, and I wondered why I ever wanted him to move in the first place. Now that I'm training for the competition and he is 2-1/2, I'm not sure he will make it to 3 because he is taking me on a trip to the end of my rope.

I know that he knows how to use the potty but he doesn't want to do it. "I'm the baby," he says.

"Don't you want to be the big boy?" I ask (beg, plead).

"No. My name is Henry. I'm the baby."

The baby can make complicated ladders out of anything to reach whatever it is I don't want him to reach. He likes to open cereal boxes and dump the contents on the floor. Of course this gets him a time-out and I make him clean up his mess, but that only stops him for a short while.

He's in the corner more than he's out of it. I used to bring him to his room for time-outs but my legs are so sore from exercising, and he gets so many time-outs, I had to change the locale to the kitchen corner.

When Rylee got a time-out she would sob and scream but stay put until it was over and she apologized for whatever she did and we moved on. She must have internalized the episodes of *Super Nanny* I always had on. She even gave herself a time-out once. Really.

Henry will do everything in his power to escape. When I tell him he's getting a time-out he says, "No, thank you." He will try to run. He will switch tactics and hug my legs and say, "I love you, Mommy." He will try to make me laugh by doing a funny little dance.

I wonder how it is possible that both kids came from the same womb.

But now that I'm doing my bikini project I'm too damn tired to do all the Tiger Mom stuff I used to do. Yes, I will read Rylee a bedtime story, but I no longer have her practice writing her ABCs in the Kumon workbook after that because I need to get downstairs and down a protein shake before it gets too late.

During the day I will take Henry to the park, but then I turn on *Umizoomi* on Nick Jr. and hope he absorbs the math lessons while I fall asleep on the couch next to him. Waking at 5 a.m. to exercise for two hours, knowing full well that I have to go back to the gym for another hour after I pick up Rylee from nursery school, completely zaps the desire to do counting lessons on my own.

The kids seem to like Less-Intense-Mom better than Tiger Mom. I'm not sure how long this will last but for now the tigeress is sleeping.

You're In A Different Place Now

I have a fear of falling, but this is not without merit. My kindergarten gym teacher told me I wouldn't fall if I looked straight ahead. Then I fell through the trampoline and said to the teacher, "Told you." I also fell through bleachers (middle school), wiped out in front of everyone going up the main ramp to the front door on a sunny day (high school), and tripped over my own bootlaces in the main lobby at my first job. (Hope the people watching the surveillance video were not laughing too hard.)

So I felt it was quite reasonable to clutch the stairwell railing for dear life when Daniel wanted me to do sprints up and down the stairs at Metroflex.

"What are you doing? Stop holding the rails!" he shouts over the latest Kayne West rap blaring at the gym.

"OK," I said, letting go of the rail and then proceeding to run at the speed of walking.

"Stop, stop, stop."

I had a feeling he wouldn't let that slide.

"You're on the stair machine almost every day. You chase your kids up and down the stairs in your house. You don't fall then, do you?"

"You don't know the depths of my clumsiness." I'm still holding the wooden rail. Bodybuilders are grunting as they pump iron. A man puts chalk on his hands and glances up at me. I'm embarrassed.

"If you trip, you're just going to land wrong on one step, right?"

I saw visions of myself falling down the stairs in slow motion ending in chipped teeth and a dentist bill.

"You're in a different place now. You're not where you were six months ago. You have more balance, you have better response time, you're not going to fall."

And I didn't.

I am in a different place now. It's like what those moms said to me last November—"It gets easier." They were right. It does get easier. *It's never easy; but it does get easier.*

These past few months I didn't ever think I'd lose the last 10 pounds. I spent hours at the gym. I had to talk myself down constantly from throwing in the towel and buying pizza for dinner. Sometimes it felt like all the gym rats were judging me and laughing at my clumsiness. But it got easier.

It's still not *easy*. Some days I just don't want to lift another set because my arms are on fire. Some days I want to revolt against green bean consumption. But it's easier.

Likewise, after a stretch of good behavior, my two-and-a-half-year-old will get into my makeup case and paint himself with my mascara and concealer, but at least he now responds better to time-outs.

Today we went to one of those child-themed haircut places, where the kids sit in stationary race cars as the stylist trims their hair. My kids were laughing and having a blast. Another mother came into the crowed place. She looked about 14 months pregnant, ready to burst, and had a son a year younger than mine, who was having an all out temper tantrum refusing to get his hair cut. The mom tried to pry her son off the hair-covered floor, her face getting as red as her maternity shirt with anger and embarrassment.

I looked at her kindly and said, "It gets easier."

This Old House

It's June. I'm at our building, sitting on the bench in the courtyard, the bench that we bought and put up together to make it seem more like a home for our tenants. Henri is eating grilled chicken fajitas from the taco place and I have my Tupperware of tilapia, green beans, and rice.

"This has been one wild ride," I said to Henri. "Remember when we first bought the place four years ago? What a piece of shit," I laughed. And it was.

It had looked like such a good investment on paper. It took forever to close, because it all happened in the months leading up to the crash and the Great Recession, but we wanted it so bad. "Make it happen, Henri," I had said.

When Rylee was 18 months old, we took a flight out so I could see what we had bought. What a sight it was. Broken beer bottles on the ground, blankets hanging over the broken windows, rusted out stairwells, wood rotted everywhere. Some of the tenants were criminals, and I feared just standing there with my baby daughter. The more we uncovered to fix something small, the more problems we found, the more money we spent, the more we wondered why we got into this mess and how we could get out.

"It had potential," Henri says laughing. "No one saw it but us."

"And look at it now. The rotted wood's been replaced by stone, the stairwells are new, the tenant units are almost done being renovated. You've done a great job, Henri. Seriously. I'm really proud of you."

He shrugs his shoulders, but I can see he is pleased.

"No, really, you did. You got mad skills my friend." I take a bite of my cold tilapia. We don't have a microwave in the office yet, but I'll buy one soon. "Remember when the ground floor used to flood with mud every time it rained because there weren't any drains?"

"It's come a long way," he chuckles, nodding his head in agreement.

The balconies are clean now. The tenants are all screened. I feel safe bringing my kids here now.

"Remember when the manager told us we were crazy to renovate this place? God, everyone thought we were crazy," he says, biting into his fajita.

"'This is the barrio,' she said, remember? And everyone told us we were wasting our money?"

"Everyone."

"And today, we can celebrate."

"Why's that?"

"Because today marks the first month we made a profit." He mirrors my smile, my relief, my sense of accomplishment.

We hold hands briefly. I note how different they look and feel now versus when we first met. Our hands used to be soft. Today they are hardened; his from a hammer and mine from pumping iron. We are both wearing our wedding rings again. It's funny—a few months ago I wanted to write a romance novel. I didn't realize I would be writing about my own love story.

"I wish we could drink champagne or something."

"Oh, we will. My show's almost here, and when it's done we can celebrate."

I look at the building's transformation around me. It's not perfect, but it seems like a metaphor for our marriage. It was more difficult than we ever expected, and sometimes it got ugly, but the foundation was strong. I guess we could have abandoned it, found a new place instead, but I'm glad we stuck with it. And I think we appreciate this place more. I think we appreciate everything more.

PIECE OF CAKE!

My daughter, Rylee, turns five tomorrow. Sure, Henri could go to the store to buy the cake, but I think we can all agree it makes way more sense to have the carb-deprived-sugar-depleted-recovering-junk-food-addict do it instead. (!?!)

June 9, 2012, 10 p.m.

OK, I just have to make it to HEB and back. It feels like driving to hell and back. Why does f**ing McDonald's have to be on the way to HEB? Why do I have to be stuck at the traffic light next to McDonald's???? I want McDonald's. I want Chicken McNuggets and not the little 6-piece meal. I want the 10-piece meal with French fries and Diet Coke and I want to supersize it. And get chocolate chip cookies too. The smell of greasy French fries permeates my car and I inhale deeply.

I want to chew off my arm, but since bikini competitions value symmetry it probably would not be a good idea to have one stumpy arm with teeth marks on it. Nine years later the light turns green and I finally get to HEB.

The lights in the store are blazing brightly and it feels like I'm entering a fun house where everything is distorted. I pass through the cereal aisle. *I want Cocoa Puffs.* I see chocolate chip granola bars. *I want those. Why am I in the cereal aisle anyway? Why am I here? Oh, yeah, cake. Find the cake. Then get out of here.*

I go to the bakery (!!!) section. *I want brownies.* They are pure chocolate joy with chocolate frosting. I see mini cupcakes with pink, blue, and yellow frosting and rainbow sprinkles. I put them in the cart for Rylee's Sunday school class. *How many calories is one mini cupcake?* I read the box. 120 calories. *If I just eat one mini cupcake and skip the 99/1 lean turkey and green beans, would my trainer ever really find out?*

What the f**k am I thinking? OF COURSE he would know—he's Daniel, and he'd kill me. And I'm stepping onstage in a bikini in two weeks.

I find the ice cream cake and put it in my cart. Mission. Accomplished. I can go home.

The phone rings. It is my husband. "Babe, can you get me potato chips while you're there? I want the ones with ridges, not the wavy ones."

ARE YOU KIDDING ME? HE WANTS ME TO GO DOWN THE CHIP AISLE???? IS HE A SADIST?

I slowly approach the chip aisle with dread, fear, and longing. Popcorn. *I want popcorn.* Tortilla chips. *I want those with salsa. I want hamburgers and hot dogs with hot dog buns. I want a Marie Callender's Chicken Pot Pie. I want fried chicken. Oh God, where are the stupid chips with the ridges???* I only see wavy. Screw him—he's getting wavy and he'll have to deal. I throw two bags of chips in the cart and go to the checkout line.

I am surrounded by high calorie, highly processed foods that say ridiculous things like "low cal," "low fat," "reduced fat." What a load of bullshit! Everything in this store clogs your arteries. *Why do I crave all this junk food so badly?*

I want cheese. I really, really want cheese.

The person in front of me is taking forever. The magazines say things like, "Lose 10 pounds FAST!" next to a picture of chocolate cake with strawberries. The tabloids are tearing Jessica Simpson to shreds for, God forbid, being pregnant and not having toned arms. *What kind of messed up society is this?*

I pay for the crap food and get in the car. I want to eat EVERYTHING. Gripping the wheel, I inhale deeply to calm myself down. I force myself to get a little perspective. I'm hungry by choice. I'm doing this for a limited period of time as part of a sports competition. But there are lots of people out there who are hungry and it's not by choice.

Moral of this story: Do not go food shopping for major celebrations two weeks out from a bikini competition. Send your husband (or sister, friend, parent, whatever) and save your energy for show prep.

EVERY 3 HOURS

Today is Wednesday, three days before the show. My mom and brother fly in from New Jersey tomorrow and my house is a flurry of activity. I've been cleaning the house (with 5" heels on), tanning, getting weird things to dehydrate myself (as is the bodybuilding custom), texting a makeup person to fit me in, and getting my nails done.

They look beautiful. But not $92 beautiful. Holy shit, Henri's going to pop a vein when he sees the bill! I put it on the credit card to delay the argument for at least a month. I just can't handle an argument on a dehydrated, empty, very tan stomach.

Henri is home, which is good, because I'm late and the babysitter has to get to her second job. Henri calls me. "You almost done? You used the cash I gave you, right?"

I garble an "umhuh" because it's not lying if it's inaudible. "On my way home," I say more clearly, then quickly hang up.

Daniel's back to his hard-ass self again. The other week when he called me out (for not drinking enough water, drinking too much Diet Pepsi, and using more than five sprays of I Can't Believe It's Not Butter) after an eight-week hiatus of saying little more than "good job," seemed to open the dam of reprimands.

Just got a seemingly innocuous text from Daniel.

Daniel: How many meals u have left? Just making sure—R u are eating every 3 hours?

Texting and driving don't mix. Plus, I haven't been spacing my meals out every three hours like I'm supposed to; I've been eating every two (OK, one and a half) hours. Know why? BECAUSE I'M HUNGRY! So I try lying by omission.

Lisa: Not sure
Daniel: I take that as a no bc u should have 2 or 3 meals left if ur first meal was at 9 . . .

He's calling me out because I was in the gym at 5 a.m., did my cardio, abs, posing practice, sauna stretch, and then went home at 8 a.m. but didn't get a chance to eat until 9 a.m. He says I have to pack a meal with me so I can eat right after cardio. But the meal I'm supposed to eat is scrambled egg whites with spinach. It tastes bad to me when it's fresh and hot. What the hell will it taste like cold and in Tupperware?

Raindrops fall on my windshield. I'm so late, and there's a cop behind me going exactly 25 mph so I can't even speed up. I'm at the light now, so I reply. It's really difficult to text with fabulous looking fake nails.

Lisa: Fine.

When wanting to end a tedious conversation, just agree with whatever the person is saying. This works for me 95% of the time.

Daniel: What does that mean?

Jesus stop bugging me! Must you always demand 100% from me!?!
I pull into my driveway and text.

Lisa: Fine! Will spread out meals.
Daniel: No need to get mad. It's just vital that u wait three hours b4 each meal and your last meal should be as soon as u go to bed.

Ooh! I want to punch him! Henri is opening the front door now. And I want to punch him too! And he didn't even do anything! I'm just so mad!

Lisa: But I'm hungry! I'm ready to chew my arm off.
Daniel: I understand . . . Trust me. We have to follow food better next time around.
Lisa: k

K. fine. Whatever. When is this competition over?

EVERY 13-1/2 MINUTES

Switching subjects completely . . . It has been an an epic battle to potty train Little Henry. Let us review the techniques I systematically tried (and failed) this past year:

- The Diaper Ceremony. (Toddler throws away all diapers in house to make that body/mind connection that babyhood is now over.)
- Pull-ups.
- Positive reinforcement, aka bribery. (I'll give you a race car if you use the toilet . . .)
- M&M's. (One M&M for pee-pee and two for number 2.)
- Negative reinforcement. (Come on . . . you don't want to be a baby do you?)
- Begging. (Please use the potty! Just this once!)
- Reverse psychology. (Fine. Don't use the potty, then.)

But nothing worked and here's why: neither of us really wanted it to work. My son heavily identified himself with being the baby, and had no interest in giving up a good thing. And, to be honest, I knew he would be my last child, and I wasn't really thrilled with the idea of him growing up. Neither of us was willing to put in the consistent effort required, so we were both left to deal with dirty diapers, which is ultimately what we deserved.

My son and I played our little "why can't he do this?" (wink, wink) game for 11 months. But now that I am staring down his third birthday, I realize I'm not doing my job as a mom by keeping him a baby. I have to help him grow up, even if he doesn't want to.

"Henry, it's time for you to be a big boy now. I want you to succeed, but I don't know when your body needs to go; only you do. But I won't let you fail, so I'm going to take you to the potty every thirteen and a half minutes so you don't have an accident."

My son gives me a look like I'm crazy. He starts to play blocks. "It's been thirteen and a half minutes! Time for the potty!" He groans. After the potty trip, he meticulously sets up his finger paints, ready for him to begin painting. "It's been thirteen and a half minutes! Time for the potty!" He stomps his foot in annoyance. He starts watching his favorite show on TV. "It's been thirteen and a half minutes! Time for the potty!" I let the TV run so he misses the ending. He grows furious to the point of tears.

"Honey, only you know when you need to go, so until you can prove to me that you can do it on your own, I'm going to have to keep interrupting you, because I really want you to succeed."

Well guess who suddenly wanted to go to the bathroom by himself? It took 11 months and 1 day of really, really wanting it.

Likewise, I talk about really "wanting" to be in control of my eating, but I pretty much outsourced that to Daniel. As much as it's been fun these last five months writing down the contents of my stomach six times a day and asking for permission to eat a slice of gluten-free toast, I think I'm ready to put on my big-girl pants too.

When Daniel told me he was moving back to Houston, I was happy that he found a good job opportunity, but I was also really scared that I would gain the weight back without having a drill sergeant trainer in my life. But it's probably a good thing for me too.

Drill sergeants are good for basic training; tearing down excuses and mental blocks and building you back up on a better foundation. I know about clean eating now. I know about strength training now. I've injected self-discipline back in my life. In short: I've graduated from boot camp. I'm gonna be fine.

STOP PICKING ON ME!

Today is Thursday, two days before the show. My mom and brother fly in tonight. Yay! It's a new day and I'm going to start it out right by sending my hard-ass trainer proof that I'm eating after cardio so he doesn't bug me. I take a pic of me eating a banana at the gym and text it to him.

Lisa: C? I ate my banana.

Mission Accomplished. I'm on my way home.

I park the car and walk inside the kitchen to make my eggs. Oh boy, Henri is holding a credit card bill.

"What's this charge for?" he asks incredulously.

"I waxed my eyebrows," I say sheepishly, pulling out the frying pan and carton of egg whites.

"Seventeen dollars to wax your eyebrows?!"

My phone starts beeping.

Daniel: Of course you would! It's your banana ☺! Did u eat ur eggs with it bc I didn't see that . . .

This isn't going the way I planned. He was supposed to be happy I was eating, not calling me out about egg whites.

Lisa: I cook them at home. I don't do cold egg whites.
How well do you think that comment went over?

Like 15 text messages with **ALL CAPS** and lots of !!!!!!!!!!!!!!!!! later, I decided it was safer to follow the meal plan. Daniel gets very pissy when you don't follow his meal plan. I'll still get heart palpitations ten years from now thinking of those texts. This is my worst meal. Ever.

Daniel: !!! Don't do that again! Eat your banana, egg whites and spinach at the same meal!!

Three exclamation points before the first word? Really?

"Why can't you just tweeze your own eyebrows? Seventeen dollars!" Henri is shaking his head.

Well if he's all fussy about $17, then I really won't tell him about the $92 fake nails. Did you know that a regular manicure is about $20 but the special *gel* nails cost, um, $92? Yeah, I didn't know that either.

My phone buzzes with a new text and Henri looks annoyed.

Daniel: Boil the eggs and eat the whites that way . . . It has to be with the protein so the carbs transfer the protein faster. It's simple. Just follow the meal plan.

Lisa: I do for everything else.

I text back as fast as I can with my pretty, sparkly, $92 fake gel nails, then put the phone down.

"I'm sorry I got my eyebrows done. It was unnecessary, I know," I say looking at him. *Please don't ask me about the cost of the manicure!* He's reading the bill and looks at costs for supplements, posing classes, and heels.

"I'm sorry," I grumble again, dealing with the stupid scrambled egg whites in the pan. If I never see an egg white again it will be too soon. My phone buzzes.

Daniel: I have told u many times that there's a reason why I have things written the way I do.

Stop getting so huffy! He gets so mad about deviations from the meal plan. I type an apology explanation as best I can with the acrylics glued to my fingertips.

Lisa: OK, so I messed up this morning. I'm like a size 1, so clearly I'm following the plan most times. Will do better tomorrow.

I put the phone on the kitchen table, scoop the eggs onto a paper plate and force myself to eat the sorry looking food before me.

"The training, the posing classes, the supplements, the bikinis, everything adds up, Lisa!"

Oh, please just let it drop, Henri! The phones buzzes so fiercely it does a little dance on the table. Oh God, do I even want to look at the message? I feel like a ping-pong ball getting smacked between the two of them.

Daniel: The size doesn't matter!! It's the muscle that I'm worried about. It's not about how small u are. U need to understand that. If u just want to be small then this sport isn't for you. It's about shaping your body to look good onstage.

Oh for f***'s sake, both of you stop picking on me!!!

Lisa: Mercy!

"OK, Henri, I'm sorry. Look, the show is over in two days and then all these expenses will go away," I say sincerely. I really shouldn't have gotten my eyebrows done. We are tight with cash. I'm really glad he didn't ask about the rockstar nails.

"It's not that seventeen dollars is expensive, it's just that it adds up with everything else," he says, planting an unforeseen kiss on my forehead. The phone buzzes once more.

Daniel: And again I am not mad. Just tryin to get u to understand.

I exhale. Just two more days . . .

THE KIDS ARE ALL RIGHT

My babies are turning into little people right before my eyes. At first it kind of frightened me at how fast they were changing and realizing how quickly I would be left behind, but now I'm really starting to like their new ages. Five and three sounds like a lot of fun, doesn't it? Little Henry has decided he no longer wants to be a baby and has been using the potty. He looks so proud of himself!

And after many sleepless nights wondering what to do about my daughter, we finally enrolled her in the (fingers crossed!) right school for her. She skipped a grade and will start in the fall as a first grader. I hope she will thrive.

I wonder what they think of my little bikini project, if they think of it at all? I think incorporating a healthy lifestyle has impacted my kids. Even though my children are very young, and we don't have lengthy conversations about health, apparently they have been watching me and absorbing things on their own.

For example, since I've been training, I switched up my own diet but kept their diet mostly the same, with the thought that I needed to fix myself before I could fix anyone else. One day we sat down for dinner and I was eating ground turkey, quinoa and asparagus and my kids were eating bow-tie pasta with butter. Rylee suddenly rose from the dinner table and went to the refrigerator.

"What are you doing?" I asked.

She came back with some leftover chicken and said, "I have gym tomorrow, so I'm going to need some extra protein with my carbs so I can run faster."

WHAT??

But on the flip side, Rylee was looking at her stomach the other day, her pink princess dress yanked up over her bellybutton as she scrutinized herself and said, "I wish my waist was smaller." Oh, God, no! Did my bikini competition make her think this way?

"Your waist is beautiful, Rylee. Why do you want it smaller?"

"Because all the Disney princesses have small waists."

Whew! Thank God it was Disney who put that crap in her head and not me!

We were sitting on the carpet next to the dining room table. How fitting the conversation happened there. It starts so young—issues of weight, issues of food. I NEVER want either of my children to go through what I did: years of yo-yo diets, self-sabotage, and doubt.

"Rylee, the size of your waist doesn't matter. It's better to be strong than just skinny. And do you know what's even more important than that?"

"What?" she asked, her eyes as open as her mind.

"Being a good person. Being kind, and honest and generous. Your waistline is going to change throughout your life, but if you can keep your character, that's what's really important, right?"

She climbed into my lap and kissed my cheek. "I love you, Mommy," she said.

Later that night, when she goes to bed, I think about her starting school in the fall. Whenever I need to work through my feelings I write. This is the letter I wrote to my daughter…

GOOD NIGHT BABY/GOOD MORNING LITTLE GIRL

Tonight I tuck you into bed, your last night as my baby. Your face is sweet and clean and innocent, unmarked yet by the world to come. Tonight I am the most important person in your life. Tonight you have only known unconditional love. Tonight you believe in fairies and stare in simple wonderment at the world that surrounds you.

Good night, my sweet baby.

Tomorrow you will wake a little girl. You will walk to your first day of school bravely, in your pretty pink dress and blond little curls and the world will enter in.

Tomorrow your friends become more prevalent in your life. But don't ever forget that the most important voice to listen to is your own.

Tomorrow you will learn that relationships are conditional and can be won and lost with speed; and sometimes you have no say in the matter.

Tomorrow you will learn the truth about fairies and you'll wonder why I lied. Until you have your own children and will want that magic to reappear.

And in not so many tomorrows you'll realize that I'm lame and don't know what I'm talking about. But don't worry; in your mid-twenties I'll seem pretty smart again. When you have your own kids, trust me, I'll seem brilliant.

Tomorrow you'll have your heart broken by some boy and I'll try to just listen and console. Your father will try to shoot him with a gun. But don't worry; I'm pretty sure it will only be a warning shot. (I'm pretty sure about that.)

Tomorrow you will break some other boy's heart. Please be kind and let him down easy. He is some other mother's son.

Tomorrow you will greet the world as your own person. Remember the lessons that I've taught you. Remember that I will always love you. And know that even when you are 100, you will always be my sweet baby.

Good morning, little girl!

Here's the world:

Now go make your mark on it.

Love,

Mom

LAST TRAINING SESSION

I go in for my training session. It's the last one before the show. It's the last one before he moves back to Houston. Rap music is blaring and there is a loud clanging of metal dumbbells being dropped to the floor by some bodybuilder.

We're not going to do any measurements because he doesn't want me to stress about anything before the show. He said I can weigh myself on the morning of the show. But weight, measurements, they don't really even matter now; I'm in the best shape of my life and I don't need a tape measure or scale to tell me that. "My Buffy Weight" looks flabby in comparison. I can bench press "My Buffy Weight."

Over by the leg extension area my new trainer, Mel, stands with her girls. Her real name is Melissa Merritt but everyone calls her Mel. She was Ms. Figure USA and won all kinds of competitions. She has an all women's bodybuilding team called Mel's Machines that I'm going to join once Daniel moves. Her girls look like supermodels. I feel intimidated as hell, but then I see Mel do some goofy dance between sets and all the girls are laughing, so it might be fun.

He motions me over to the picnic table. "Your mom and brother are in town now?"

"Yeah, they came last night."

"What do they think?"

"They couldn't believe how much weight I lost, even since the reunion last month."

"Your mom thinks you're too thin, doesn't she?" he smiles.

"Yeah," I say. *Whoa, now he can read my mother's mind too. He really is a Jedi.*

"Take a picture, because this will be the thinnest you'll ever be. Then we start growing muscle on you. You'll weigh a little more, but you'll look better. Oh, here, before I forget." He pulls out the rough draft of my book I gave him at the photo shoot we all did for the blog and, hopefully, the cover of this book. (Thank you Caroline Poe for taking the pictures; you're awesome!)

I felt it was only fair to show him a copy of the manuscript, since he's in a lot of it. I promised him that if he didn't like it, I would change his name to something like Joe the Trainer. I'm nervous.

"What do you think?" I ask cautiously.

"It's got your personality stamped all over it."

"Well that's good, since I wrote it."

"Seems like you learned some things."

"Yeah. Eat clean, train dirty."

"I like that you wrote about wanting a trainer to deliver results and not just be a friend."

"It's true."

He pauses, then, "How do you remember all that stuff? I talk all day long and nobody ever listens to me."

"I'm a writer and an actor. I hear conversations like dialogue from a movie. If that makes sense." I can see it doesn't make sense to him, but I don't know how to explain it better.

"So why do you think it was different this time? Why do you think you finally reached your goal?"

"I think it was the timing of everything. No one ever gave me a cheater's weekend and let me decide on my own that I went overboard. And then when you told me I didn't have the mental strength to do this, well that just pissed me off to no end. (He laughs.) Then seeing all those women a few weeks later at the Shredder, a lot of them mothers, some of them older than me, looking so ripped and confident, I thought, 'If they can do it, I can too.'"

He nodded his head, taking it in. "Your book—it's kind of addictive."

"That's just because you're in it."

"I've never been in a book before. That's kind of cool."

"See? Now you have bragging rights forever. 'I'm such a good trainer, my client wrote a book about me.'"

He laughs again. "All right, let's get started." We walk to the FreeMotion press. I'm doing a full upper body workout today.

"So you want to be a trainer," he said. I forgot I mentioned that to him last week. "You have to know what you're talking about," he challenges.

"And clearly, I don't," I retort, "which is why I'm going to take the NASM course."

He starts putting weights on the machine.

"Or maybe not," I confess. "I don't know if I'd make a good trainer."

"Why do you say that?" he asks looking up, mildly curious.

"I think it might drive me nuts to have to deal all day with people who cheat on their diets." He stops putting the weights on the machine midair and gives me that look of his.

"I've apologized to you on numerous occasions for being myself!" I said, hands on my hips.

He broke a smile despite himself. "You just have to be a people person, that's all."

I shrug my shoulders. I'm pretty sure there's more to it than that. See, I don't want to just be a trainer; I want to be a *good* trainer. Over the past eight years I've worked on and off with six different trainers, Daniel being the sixth. With the other trainers I sort of got healthier for a little while and got a little muscle tone, but it went away when the sessions were used up, and I began to yo-yo diet again.

Daniel managed to break through my mental blocks and now I'm actually *healthy* and wanting to make this my lifestyle, even though he's moving away. I feel like I can do this now without him. And that's the kind of trainer I want to be. I want people who are unhealthy to change their lives and become well, even after the sessions are done, and I don't know if I can do that. But I don't say any of this. I say nothing.

He has a broad smile on his face that is laughing at me. "When you met me you didn't know shit about shit!"

Ah, Daniel, subtle as an atomic weapon. He says he's a Southern boy but I think in a past life he must have been from Jersey.

"But look what happened," he continued. "You started seeing results, you fell in love with the sport, we built a relationship, and now you trust me. You followed me to the gym over here. I'm not a miracle worker. It's just diet and exercise that gets you in shape."

"I guess."

"We've been training how long? Half a year?"

I do the calculations in my mind. "Almost five months."

"I feel like I've known you forever. Like I know your husband, your kids. You know stuff about me. It's just listening. You're a people person; you're going to love being a trainer."

He was an unlikely mentor. At first I completely wrote him off. I didn't trust him. I battled him at every chance. He called me out on every bullshit lie and excuse as soon as it rolled off my tongue. Sometimes I hated him. For a while he intimidated the hell out of me. But he delivered on every promise he made and I'm in the best shape of my life. Now we laugh about the first couple of months.

"I'm so sorry I was such a pain-in-the-ass client."

"It's a process," he laughed.

After our session I start to head out to my car, but he calls me back. As luck would have it, as if destined by the universe, the NASM certification textbooks he loaned to another person were at the counter. And now I'm studying them.

At the desk I left him a birthday card with Obama on it (he's a Republican, so I had to mess with him) and a T-shirt that said "Badass Trainer."

Someday when I am a trainer I hope that pain-in-the-ass clients will tell me that they sometimes hated me, and that they were sometimes intimidated by me, but that I helped them break down their own walls to become healthy. Someday I hope to become a mentor.

ATHLETE'S MEETING

It's Friday night. My mom and brother are watching the kids so Henri and I can go to the athlete's meeting held at a local hotel. I'm so excited I'm bouncing off the walls. The men get weighed in and the women get their height measured. (Thank God the women don't get weighed in—can you imagine the orange tanning smears from all the tears!?!)

It is all very exciting. I'm sitting in front with the girls from my posing class. They are all on Adela's team and are dressed in really hot cocktail dresses. I had just gotten my spray on tan fifteen minutes before the check-in and am wearing sweatpants, flip flops and my Moms Kick Butt tank top.

I know that the only reason I'm sitting there is because Daniel's girlfriend, Maria, is on the team and she invited me to sit with them. I wonder what it's like to be on a team? They're all really nice. Most of them have won trophies before. Maybe someday I'll win one too. But right now I feel like I've earned something just getting to the athlete's meeting, because for the first time in my life I actually feel like an athlete; I actually look like what an athlete looks like, strong and easy within my own skin.

Now it's time to sit down. The promoters tell us what time to check in the next day and have pro bodybuilders show us which poses are allowed. You can tell a lot of people know each other. Adela is speaking on the microphone, thanking sponsors. She asks, "Who is doing their first show tomorrow?"

I raise my hand, as do a dozen or so others. The crowd cheers. Tomorrow everyone competes, tonight we are part of the same tribe. We are a subset of the Clan of the Gym Rats. We are Bodybuilders. We eat clean, lift heavy, and can rock that bikini.

Then the meeting part is over and it feels exactly like being in Catholic high school again—the men line up on one side and the women line up on the other side, only instead of checking the skirt length the officials check your bikini, and if it is too risqué you are not allowed to walk onstage. (FYI— no one was told their bikini was too risqué.)

As the meeting closes I get a text.

Daniel: A surprise for you. Go to a good restaurant and order a steak and mashed potatoes. But nothing to drink.
Lisa: STEAK?!?!?!? FOR REAL?!?!?

Is he just messing with me? That would be rather cruel in my carb-depleted, water-depleted state.

Daniel: Enjoy ☺

It felt like Henri and I were on a real date.

Show Day

Today is show day!!! I walk into the bathroom and freak out when I look into the mirror and see an orange woman staring back at me; then I remember the spray on tan. The tanning lady who sprayed me last night told me to put toilet paper into the bowl before going to the bathroom so nothing would splatter. This is such a weird sport. She also told me that one time a client came to the show wearing a sweatshirt and a panicked expression. I guess the woman's husband liked to cuddle, and there were giant handprints on her ta-tas. That made me giggle. She was able to do some touch up spray on her.

I take off my clothes, like I do every day, and stand on the scale. I'm exactly 100 pounds, just like Daniel predicted. I take a picture of the readout with my cell phone, since this is the lightest I will ever be. What's strange, though, is that I'm OK with the fact that I'm going be a little heavier soon, because I know it's going to be muscle. I no longer want to be 99 pounds soaking wet; I want to be stronger and I'm excited for the future.

But back to present time. ... Check-in was at 7:30 a.m., but like a dumbass I went to the wrong high school. 'Cause how many high schools could there possibly be in Pflugerville, Texas, population 12 people, right? Geez, sometimes I feel like the Lucy Ricardo of women's bodybuilding. Thank God Henri was driving, because he got me there just in time to get my number, and now it's just hours and hours and HOURS of waiting until my division is called.

Backstage is mobbed with the most fantastically gorgeous people you could possibly imagine, and I know a thing or two about pretty people—I lived in Los Angeles. There are water bottles around, but nobody drinks a sip. Groups of women are huddled by electrical outlets to curl their hair. Men are pumping iron on floors lined with paper so the body oil doesn't damage the tile.

Maria had given me the name of her makeup person, Eden, who has a table set up in the main holding area. I'm nervous and trying not to be needy. I brought a notebook with me and scribble down my thoughts. Here they are (in no particular order):

- I'm thirsty.
- Why does Masters Bikini have to go dead last? There will be no one left in the audience because everyone gets to leave prejudging after their class is done.
- The bathroom smells like spray tan and asparagus pee.

- I hope I don't fall onstage.
- This is the best sport ever. I never knew I could be this in shape.
- I hope I don't gain the weight back. I don't think I will. I think . . . No. I *know* I'll be OK.

And now . . . it's time. I'm standing in my heels next to the other women. You can pretty easily pick out the top five women. I'm not there. *Yet.* But I do look like I belong onstage and not hiding in the wings.

I do my little bikini walk, the one I've practiced a million times. I hear Henri calling out my number and my mom, brother and Regina cheer. It's like I have my own little pep rally, and I'm so thankful that they are here, and so supportive of my crazy little ideas.

Maria's in the audience now with Daniel, and I hear her calling out to me, "Keep it tight, Lisa! Arch your back!"

Oops! I arch my back as far as I can, and try to remain balanced. And smile.

A few seconds later it's done.

Five months, fifty pounds, hundreds of dirty Tupperware containers in the sink, and countless times I questioned my sanity, resolve, and ability to finish, then a teensy ten seconds under the stage lights later and it's all over.

Of course I didn't win for a plethora of reasons: It was my first competition, so I was nervous and it showed big time in my posing; I was still getting comfortable in my new, looser skin (I dropped 50 pounds faster than my skin could keep up); and for the life of me, I couldn't balance in those dang 5″ heels. Don't get me wrong—there are lots of Cinderella stories out there, but I'm not one of them.

But training to win, and then losing, was actually very good for me. I would have never stopped cheating on my diet, and trained as hard as I did, if I didn't think there was a chance of winning. So it did make me push myself beyond my own mental limits. And as far as failing goes, it had been a long, long while since the last time I really put my neck on the line for something and gave my absolute 100%.

Losing sucks. I cried even. But you know what? I didn't die. And I'm not as afraid of failing (or trying) as I was before.

After the show Daniel said to me, "It's not about going home with a trophy, or a sword, or a medal. You set goals and you stuck with them to the end. You did it, Lisa."

I'm happy I didn't quit on myself. I'm happy I stepped on the stage. And I'm happy I have made *progress*. I'm only really competing against myself, anyway. And as for winning, I have a secret. I will never have a *Cinderella* story. Because *my* story is the *Little Engine That Could.* "I think I can. I think I can. I know I can! I KNOW I CAN!"

And one day, I'll win a trophy. I'll win it for me. And I'll know that I've earned it.

TROPHY WIFE

After the show, Mom and my brother, Dennis, get in the car with Henri, and I get in Regina's car. We are going to celebrate with dinner at my favorite Italian restaurant. God, I've missed pasta. And wine. And dessert. But I just get one cheat week and then it's back to training again. I'm already thinking about how I can improve for the next show.

I spy the water bottle. "Oh, can I have a sip?"

"Drink away," Regina says. I down almost the entire bottle in the first sip. "Thirsty?"

"Very. Distilled water will do that to you. So, what did you think?"

"You looked amazing, but I couldn't help wondering, 'If I ate a roast beef sandwich in the audience, would I be attacked?'" she giggled.

"Oh you would be *devoured*. We are all starving right now." We get on I-35S and travel past Hester's Crossing.

"That's where I got my tan," I said pointing out the tanning salon.

"You look like a new race of person."

"I know. It's weird huh? It's a weird sport."

"You love it."

"I *love* it, Regina. I love this sport."

"Of course you do. It's weirdly complicated enough to hold your attention." She puts on her blinker and switches lanes. I have a half grin glued to my face. I can't believe it's over. "You look good, and I don't mean in a lustful way that your husband would look at you, I mean you look *happy*. It's not even about being thin, although, it's great that you've lost weight. I see you in that picture on your blog, where you're with your family, and your whole carriage is different. I see how you hold your shoulders back now. I just see that my friend looks confident now."

I'm beaming from ear to ear.

Dinner was fantastic. Everything smelled good. The food tasted better, probably because it was a completely sanctioned cheat meal. My mother said I looked too thin, and my brother and Henri decided they wanted to do a bodybuilding competition too.

We got home and said goodnight to everyone. I scorched myself in the shower trying to become a more regular shade of human. Wrapping myself in a towel, it was just me and Henri again.

"All right, Traugott," he said eyeing me. "So what was this whole bodybuilding thing really about?"

"I thought you were going to cheat on me."

"WHAT? Why on earth would you think that?" he asked, genuinely shocked.

"Because you said you would always love me but you weren't attracted to me."

"I said that?"

"Yes."

"Yeah . . . I say a lot of stupid things. I'm sorry. But, if it made you do this, maybe I'm not so sorry I said it."

"Let me rephrase. That's why I *started* going to the gym. I thought you were going to cheat on me. If I lost weight maybe you wouldn't. If you did anyway, at least I would be in good enough shape to fit into my clothes again, and get an office job. That was my thought, anyway. But once I started lifting, it stopped being about you, and it started being about me. I love being strong. I feel so much more in control of my life again."

"It's funny; before you started training I thought *you* were going to have an affair on *me*."

"WHAT? Why?"

"Because you had such low self-esteem. I didn't even recognize you as the girl I fell in love with. Sometimes when women gain weight and feel bad about themselves they have an affair with the first guy that tells them they're perfect."

"I've never, ever, heard that story before."

"Don't get me wrong; I think it's awesome you lost weight. I'm more attracted to you, but it's not just because you're thinner. You're confident again, and that's what makes you sexy. That's what I missed."

He wraps his arms around me. My hair is dripping on his arms.

"Confidence I have. Now I just need to keep training so I can eventually place and you can tell your friends that you literally have a trophy wife."

"Oh I have something even better than a trophy wife."

"Oh yeah?"

"Yeah. I have a successful woman."

SHE'S LOSING IT!
TIPS AND TRICKS

Top 10 Things I Learned About Female Bodybuilding

10. This sport is crazy expensive!
9. The Secret to Being Thin is the 90/10 Rule. It's 90% diet, 10% exercise.
8. OK, I lied. The Secret to a Bikini Body is the 90/30 Rule. OMG you have to diet and work out 120%!!! Holy s**t I LIVED at the gym the last three weeks.
7. When you are tanning on a tanning bed, you have to rotate like a rotisserie chicken or else your sides will look white.
6. When you are on your heavy lifting days, listen to 2Pac. Sometimes a mommy just needs her gangsta rap. Thug life baby.
5. Strike a Pose! It's all about swagger and sassiness. And I learned that . . . um . . . I got no game. Getting a strip tease video helps. Totally fun, only $7, and . . . um . . . my husband likes it too. Hee hee.
4. If you are married and your husband doesn't want to pay for the training sessions, tell him that bodybuilding will make you look like a Victoria's Secret model. That really worked for me.
3. This is a mental game. I thought bodybuilding was just about lifting weights. It's not. It requires focus, self-discipline, and mental strength to push you beyond all limits. And when you do break through your mental blocks, my God do you feel powerful.
2. Don't try this alone. You need a trainer who knows about competitive bodybuilding. And if you are like me, it helps to hire someone who is a hard-ass like Daniel.
1. Train to Win and when you walk on that stage, no matter what the judges say, just know you have already won.

SHE'S LOSING IT!—THE BIKINI DIET

Meal 1   **Pre-Workout**
1 scoop Isopure with 12 oz. water (This is a protein shake powder. I get chocolate—it's actually really yummy.)
1/2 cup pineapple
6–8 whole roasted, unsalted almonds

Meal 2   **Breakfast**
1/2 cup (dry) oatmeal (This should be the old fashioned kind, not instant.)
1 cup blueberries (Note: I usually eat this with my yogurt for AM snack.)
Scrambled eggs made with: 3 egg whites, 1 egg (with yolk), 1 cup raw spinach

Meal 3   **AM Snack**
1/2 cup Greek yogurt 1/2 cup strawberries

Meal 4   **Lunch**
3 oz. chicken breast (Weight is 3 oz. *before* cooking.)
1/4 cup (dry) quinoa (A type of grain found in the rice section of your grocery store.)
2 cups veggies (broccoli, green beans, asparagus—GREEN ONLY, fresh would be best)

Meal 5   **PM Snack**
Meal replacement protein shake (NOTE: Daniel told me not to do this while I'm in the losing weight stage. This only gets added when I'm growing muscle mass.)

Meal 6   **Dinner**
Choice of 3 oz. chicken breast/4 oz. tilapia/3 oz. lean beef
1/4 cup (dry) quinoa
2 cups mixed salad with 1 tbsp. olive oil, 1/2 lemon squeezed

Meal 7   **Late Night Snack**
1-1/2 cups fresh veggies (cucumbers, carrots, green peppers, etc.)
1/2 small avocado (I make guacamole and dip cucumbers in it)

General Notes
- Use any spices and herbs you want; stay away from seasonings because they are high in sodium.
- No soda (not even diet!), No juice, No milk, No coffee (come on, really?). Just water and/or green tea.

I found the diet very filling; sometimes I couldn't finish eating everything on the plan. I tried really hard not to cheat, but I confess to being human a few times. Overall, however, it was pretty easy to follow.

Please note: *This blog is written as a source of information only. The information contained in this blog should by no means be considered a substitute for the advice of a qualified medical professional, who should always be consulted before beginning any new diet, exercise or other health program. We expressly disclaim responsibility for any adverse effects arising from the use or application of the information contained herein.*

FOOD PREP

Everyone wonders about the diet, and how I fit cooking and eating six times a day into my schedule, so here goes. You know that phrase, "It's simple, but it ain't easy"? That would apply to the tenets of Clean Eating. There are variations among the Clean Eating disciples, but here are the basic principles with respect to bodybuilding:

1. Eat six times per day, every two to three hours.
2. Drink water instead of soda, milk, juice, coffee, etc.
3. Fruit is to be eaten in the morning.
4. Food should be unprocessed and without any added preservatives.
5. Stick to the perimeter of the grocery store to do your shopping (produce, meats, eggs) and stay away from the middle aisles where the fat-free cookies live.
6. Avoid sugar completely.
7. Carbohydrates should be complex and unprocessed. Examples: brown rice, old fashioned oats, quinoa, sweet potatoes.
8. Vegetables should be included in most of your meals, and they should be fresh, not canned or frozen. Examples: green beans, asparagus, zucchini, green peppers, red peppers, spinach, onions.
9. Dairy is kept to a minimum, like *maybe* Greek yogurt if your trainer is feeling generous, and it might be in your protein shake, depending which one(s) your trainer has you drinking.
10. Fats are limited to healthy fats in low dosages. Examples: 1/4 small avocado or 2 tbsp olive oil. When cooking, you can use butter-flavored spray so your food doesn't stick to the pan.
11. No alcohol, junk food, fast food or fried food, unless you paid off your trainer and he grants you a Cheat Meal. (Cheat Meals are subject to certain provisions, including (but not limited to) the total whims of your trainer, the timing of the cheat in relation to your show date, the timing of the cheat in relation to the time of day you eat it, and how much preemptive cardio you are willing to do before said cheat.)

Once you have mastered these rules, it is time to start cooking. These are the things I have with me when I cook:

1. Scale to weigh my meat
2. Measuring cups to measure out the carbs
3. Lots of Tupperware

I usually have two pans cooking up my meat, one pot boiling my green beans, and another boiling up the rice. As the food is finished cooking, it becomes one giant assembly line where I dole out 3 oz. of chicken, 1/2 cup rice and 1 cup green beans into as many containers as I can. Food I can eat in the same week goes in the fridge and everything else goes in the freezer. The process takes about 1–2 hours, depending on how far ahead I want to stock up my meals and I try to do it when the kids are napping or playing outside where I can keep an eye on them.

Overall, it has been very helpful for me to cook ahead, because I don't have to think about what my next meal is, I only have to clean the pots and pans once a week, and I'm prepared if I'm going to be running errands all day.

THE SECRET TO BEING THIN

Want to know the secret to being thin in my humble opinion? **It's 90% diet and 10% exercise**. Call it the **90/10 Rule**.

It's 90% Food

A bikini body is 90% diet. Seriously. I used to think that the diet-exercise ratio was a 50/50 thing. It's not. I know it's not because I ran a half marathon even though I was totally overweight. There is such a thing as "Fit Fat." The process of following the bodybuilding meal plan taught me that being fit minus the fat was absolutely possible, even for me. I'm telling you—if you eat "clean" you will be 90% to your bikini body goal. And it happens a lot faster than you would think.

1. **Eat "clean."** Cook like your grandma did. Avoid processed foods, stick to the perimeter of the grocery store when grocery shopping, and eat a good mix of proteins, vegetables, and complex carbohydrates. Eating clean isn't really that hard. If you are a normal person, I guess the first two weeks of eating clean suck. If you are a hard-core junk food junkie like me, it took two *months* to get used to the clean food mantra. But if I can do it, you can do it. Quinoa actually tastes good. Green beans are growing on me. I Can't Believe It's Not Butter Spray makes everything taste better.

2. **It's better to eat six smaller meals per day versus three big meals per day**. Here is an analogy: Think of your metabolism as a fireplace. If you put in three heavy logs the fire will take longer to catch on and it takes a lot of effort to heat the room. But, if you put in six small bundles of wood and kindling the fire starts up faster and burns more consistently.

3. **Measure your food.** Buy a food scale. I got mine at the grocery store for about $20. I used to think that just cutting a chicken breast in half was the right portion, but when working to obtain a bikini body, size does matter. Sometimes that chicken breast needs to be cut into thirds or quarters if the butcher is feeling generous that day. Also, sweet potatoes have such odd shapes it's really tricky to know where to slice to get exactly 4 ounces. Use measuring cups to make sure you don't go overboard when doling out your carbs.

4. **Keep a food journal.** All vegetables are not created equal. Sweet peas and carrots have a lot of sugar in them. Who knew? Go for fresh veggies instead of canned to avoid the added sodium and preservatives. Want to really know how your favorites stack up in the veggie wars? Keep a food journal and track the calories.

5. **Hold yourself accountable.** This was a key component for me. I outsourced this task to Daniel. You could ask a friend to check up on you, or use one of the many online sites and apps available to chart your progress. Writing a fitness blog helps too…

It's 10% Exercise

A bikini body is only 10% exercise. In a nutshell, if you just diet and don't exercise, you will have a smaller version of your frumpy body. If you just exercise and don't adjust your diet, you will have a svelte body completely hidden under a layer of fat. Combine the two and presto! Bikini body!

1. **CARDIO, CARDIO, CARDIO.** Cardio is the key to burning off the layer of fat. (Combined with eating healthy, of course.) I thought you had to do high intensity sprints and such for this to work. Not so! Daniel has me doing a combination of high intensity and low intensity cardio workouts. When I first started and was grossly out of shape, he only had me do cardio 40 minutes, three days a week to build up stamina. When I am preparing for a competition and want to lose weight, I increase my cardio to 50 minutes per day, six days per week. In the off-season, when I am looking to add lean muscle mass, I reduce my cardio back to 40 minutes three times per week.

2. **Divide and conquer for faster muscle growth**. When you lift weights you are actually tearing your muscle tissues. They need at least a day to recover and rebuild themselves into the new and improved stronger versions. Thus, it is important to focus on different muscle groups each day. A sample rotation might be:

    a. Mondays = back and biceps
    b. Tuesdays = legs and butt
    c. Wednesday = abdominals
    d. Thursday = chest and triceps
    e. Friday = take a rest!

    Extra tip: You might hear fancy lingo around the gym like, "Yeah, I'm doing a 5-2 split." That just means you're lifting weights five days per week and resting two days. But it *sounds* really cool, so make sure you say it in front of some newbie who has no idea what you're talking about.

3. **Form is King.** When done correctly, exercising will make your body look like beautifully sculpted statue. When done wrong it will give you a doctor/chiropractor bill. I injured myself the first month because (1) I was too busy talking to my friend instead of paying attention to what I was doing, (2) the weight I lifted was too heavy, and (3) I continued lifting even when my shoulder didn't feel right. These are all rookie mistakes with easy solutions. First, until you know the proper form for each exercise, hold off on the socializing and concentrate on basics like posture, grip, and foot position. Second, lighter weights lifted properly are more effective at growing muscle mass than super heavy weights flung up in a Hail Mary effort where you throw out your back. Third, if it hurts when you lift, (beyond it just feeling heavy) listen to your body. Pain is your muscle screaming at you, "You're doing it wrong! Stop!"

4. **Stretching Is Your Friend.** Stretching helps to loosen the muscles from their contracted state. Stretching increases flexibility, which in turn reduces the risk for injury. It also feels really great when you do it in the sauna while listing to the more mellow love ballads from U2's greatest hits CD.

5. **Get a Good Trainer.** Trainers are expensive. I know. But even if you can just get five sessions to learn basic exercises for each muscle group, their expertise is worth it. When you are looking for a trainer, make sure they are certified so they can teach you proper form. If you are training for a specific sport, ask for a trainer who specializes in that area. Personalities matter too. Are you looking for a drill sergeant or a cheerleader? Find someone you can communicate with.

And here's the final secret: **You have to want it.**

Just because you know what to eat and how to exercise, doesn't mean you'll do it. You have to want to be healthy more than you want those chips at your friend's party. Your desire to be fit has to outweigh your desire to roll over in bed on a cold morning when you don't feel like working out.

Maybe you start eating clean and exercising because your doctor told you to, or your boyfriend said something about your weight, or you feel like the media is pressuring you to be a certain size, but the only person that is going to keep you staying healthy is you.

Do this for yourself. You're worth it.

THE REAL CO$T OF BODYBUILDING

If you are my husband please don't read this post.

While updating my personal finances, I stumbled across all the receipts from my bodybuilding competition and thought you might be interested in knowing the true costs of this sport.

One of my annoying endearing personality quirks is that when I have a very strong idea in my head to do something (i.e., run a marathon, put on a fundraiser for 700 people, lose 50 pounds via entering a bikini competition, etc.) I tend to jump right in doing very little no research first. This annoying endearing quality drives my very budget-conscious analytical husband crazy. Here's how this works:

> CHRIS (a very fit personal trainer): I'm going to enter a bikini competition in April.
> LISA (BMI = borderline obese): I'm in.

That was my research . . .

In defense of myself, I knew the **results** I wanted—a bikini body. I had no idea what was involved in getting there. Perhaps if I had known I never would have done it, and that would have been a shame, as the results went well beyond a nice physique. I learned about nutrition, gained self-confidence, and am considering a new career path as a personal trainer. Plus, I've gained so many new friends from this sport!

But if you are curious, and more analytical than "I'm in," below is a cost breakdown for you.

Again, if you are my husband stop reading right now. Ends justify the means!!!

1st Competition Costs

Personal training sessions at commercial gym for 6 months	**$1,700**
Gym membership fees	**$180**
Supplements	**$900**
Weird-top-secret-bodybuilder-stuff my trainer had me buy but I'm not allowed to post details about	**$350**
Weird-top-secret-gluten-free-bison-meat-type-food above and beyond "normal" healthy food	**$200**
New wardrobe 'cause I lost 50 pounds	**$200** (I shop at Walmart)
Posing classes (yes, you need them)	**$280**
2 posing bikinis	**$210** (I got off kind of cheap on this one. I bought off E-bay. Some women spend $300-$600 per suit.)
5" heels	**$65*** (I bought the wrong shoes so add another $95 for a total of $160)
Tanning salon—base tan + bronzer	**$190**
NPC card	**$100**
Entrance fee for competition	**$85** per division (I just did Bikini Masters Division—that's fancy for "old chicks")
Manicure/Pedicure	**$92** (Did you know that "gels" cost a bazillion times more than just a regular manicure? Here's where that "research" thing might have come in handy . . .)
Wax eyebrows	**$17** (This was totally unnecessary, but when you just put $92 on your credit card to get gel nails, why not go for pretty eyebrows too?)

Photo shoot for the blog three weeks before the competition	**$0** (Sponsored!! THANK YOU CAROLINE POE PHOTOGRAPHY!!!)
Spray on tan night before the competition	**$150**
Hair and makeup day of the competition	**$150**
Tickets for my husband to see the pre-show + night show	**$135**
Total cost: first competition	**$5,099 = $849/mo.**

Having a bikini body without plastic surgery? *Priceless!* And hey, this sport's cheaper than golf . . .

AND . . . .HE READ IT

You knew it was coming, right? My husband, Henri, saw the post about how much money we spent on bodybuilding this past year. So here's how that conversation went down:

I'm typing up my blog post, surrounded by receipts from various gyms and supplement stores.

"What are you doing?" asks my husband.

I spin in my office chair, blocking the view of my computer.

"Nothing . . . So how much does it cost to play golf?"

"What do you mean?" He takes a sip of his Pepsi.

"Like, if golf were your sport of choice, what would you pay?"

"Oh, gosh, depending on the club you join, it could cost one hundred thousand dollars plus annual membership fees."

"Wow! *That's a lot!* But I'm not talking Beverly Hills. Just a regular old golf club. How much?" *(See how reasonable I can be, not even asking for the most expensive scenario?)*

"Well, maybe like two to four thousand dollars for a local place, plus thirty to sixty dollars each time you want to play."

"You'd play what, like once a week?" *(Yeah, right! A golf person just playing once a week!)*

"Well, if you want to improve your game you'd play at least twice a week. Why are you asking me about golf?" He puts his drink down on the desk and I remain planted in front of the computer screen.

"Remember back when we were both working, and didn't have kids, and I got you golf lessons for a birthday gift? Do you remember how much that cost?"

"I think you paid seven or eight hundred dollars for six lessons."

"Wow, I was *soooo* generous! That's a lot for just six lessons. To get good at the game, you'd probably need way more than six lessons. And let's assume you're new to the sport. How much for a set of golf clubs?"

He cocks his head to the side and stares at me.

I smile back sweetly.

"You could probably get a nice starter set on eBay or something for two thousand dollars. You're going to play golf now? You're going to blog about golf?"

"So, that's easily fifteen thousand dollars over the course of, say five months, right?" I'm in control and totally nonchalant, having just proved my case.

"Yeah. It's an expensive sport . . ." He is thoroughly confused by this conversation.

"Guess how much it cost me to do my first bodybuilding competition last year?" My voice sounds about three octaves higher than it should. So much for confidence proving my case. I could never be a trial lawyer.

"I don't know. Two or three thousand dollars?" He shrugs.

He's going to read it anyway, so I just point to my computer screen and his eyes are knitted as they scan calculations. When they reach the total his eyes open pretty wide. Not Whoopi Goldberg wide, but pretty wide.

"It was about five thousand dollars," I say, then add quickly, "but I'm just saying, aren't you glad I took up bodybuilding instead of golf?"

"Honey, I know bodybuilding is expensive; I used to do it. Why do you think I kept freaking out every time the credit card bill came in? But you got healthy and learned about nutrition. All the fad diets you tried in the past never lasted. For whatever reason, this time it stuck. You lost fifty pounds and you've changed your lifestyle. You're changing the way our kids view food, so maybe they won't have to go through all the yo-yo crap you did."

"You're not mad?" I'm biting my thumbnail. It was a lot of money to put on a credit card.

"Of course not. How are you going to amortize five thousand dollars over the course of a lifetime?" He gives me a kiss and I melt. "But it's good you're going to be working again. This bodybuilding s*** is expensive."

FINAL BLOGGER CHALLENGE: WRITE A LETTER TO YOUR FORMER SELF

DEAR FORMER ME

My heart aches watching you sobbing in your car at Rylee's nursery school that November, tears spilling over your fingers and wetting the steering wheel you were gripping so tightly.

Of course you were crying—your life was a mess: 50 pounds overweight, your marriage on the rocks, business failing, stressed over the kids. The world was collapsing around you and you felt so lost and alone.

Well, I want to tell you a few things. First, it gets better.

It's been two years since your first show and you've never gained the weight back. In fact, you're in the best shape of your life, and you are training for your fourth competition on an all women's bodybuilding team. You're celebrating your 40th birthday by not only entering the fitness division (doing gymnastics), but also by taking a beginners pole-dancing class. (How's that for sassiness, Little Miss I-Got-No-Game?)

The kids survived starting school, the business is making a profit, and you and your husband are celebrating your 10th wedding anniversary this year. Your little blog (and Facebook & tweets) reaches thousands, and you (!!) are now a personal trainer. Whoa.

Second (time for a little tough love here), you are better than you are behaving right now. Not talking to your husband, leaving the mail unopened so you don't have to look at the bills you need to pay, eating whatever is in front of you without even tasting it—in the words of Dr. Phil, "How's that working for you?" Clearly, it's not. Closing your eyes to your problems does not make them go away; you have to face them, even though you don't want to.

Finally, self esteem is earned, not given. Do you know how you get self esteem? You do hard things. You do things outside your comfort zone. Like start a blog. Like get over your body image issues, and walk onstage in a bikini. As your confidence grows, you will be able to be strong in other areas of your life too.

Lisa, you are not the person you were two Novembers ago. You are not crying now. You are stronger. You are healthier. You are happy again.

Love,
Lisa from today

P.S.—I'm not going to sugarcoat this. Turning 40 kinda sucks, so here are some useful techniques to handle the situation:

- **Get bangs.** Tell people it's to look like Taylor Swift. Real reason? $5 haircut = way more affordable than Botox for covering forehead wrinkles.
- **Hire a personal trainer younger than you.** He will teach you important things such as what TTYL means, and the difference between "Shawty" and "Shortie."
- **Ask your husband to run ahead and pay the bouncer to card you.** This is particularly effective if it is done in front of friends in their 30s, and you are the only one carded.

P.P.S.—While prepping for my third competition, something interesting happened: my husband grew love handles. I mentioned to him on several occasions about the affordability of a gym membership and he said, "Why do you keep pressuring me to go to the gym? Yeah, I've put on a little weight, but what, do I disgust you or something???"

"Oh, Henri," I said, "I will *always* love you . . ."

Aren't paybacks awesome?

Teaser—She's Building It! (Trolls & Miracles)

I'm not one to toot my own horn, but when you state your fitness goals aloud and not one but *two* personal trainers use the word *miracle* in response, well that's pretty special. With Daniel it was, "Hey, Daniel, I'd like to perform an Operation Ass Lift before my next competition," and his response was (this is an actual quote here) "I'm not a miracle worker."

Yesterday I told Mel, "I would like to do the Texas Shredder in April in the figure division and aim for fifth place," and her response was, "Well sometimes miracles do happen, but let's aim for the Adela in June."

In situations like these I find that eating the frosting directly out of the cup with a plastic spoon works best (that way you don't have to clean the spoon, you just toss it when you're done.) And it's totally OK to eat frosting now because I won't be standing onstage in a bikini for at least six months. Secretly this terrifies me and here's why.

Two weeks before my first competition someone (and just for the sake of argument let's say that that "someone" lives in a swamp in Florida) said, *"I'll bet she gains all the weight back after her reunion."* And a little piece of me believed her.

Why did she say this? I don't know. Maybe she was having a bad day and she viewed my exercise success as her own exercise failure. Or maybe she knew me for a while, had watched me yo-yo diet through the years, and thought me gaining weight was a sure thing to bet on and gain some Christmas money. Or maybe she's just a grumpy old troll who asks men three riddles before they cross over the bridge and into her vagina. I don't know.

But here's the thing—I really need to not listen to her. Who cares what she thinks?

Mel must have seen the panic in my eyes when she told me to aim for June and not April. "The judges are going to want to see improvements, not the same package in a different bikini. You make your gains in the off-season. I have to see how your muscles respond. I have to see how your body reacts to the new diet. I know you're a hard worker, but there's no point in doing competitions all year when you're not ready."

Mel's right: I'm not ready yet. Troll is wrong: I'm not going to gain back all the weight I carried before my first competition.

And I do believe that miracles can happen. Probably not by April, but over time I can work at improving my physique; after all, that's what bodybuilding is all about. And over time I'll improve other parts of myself that need a little work too (like caring what everyone thinks and turning to frosting in moments of stress); after all, you're more than just your body parts.

Trolls of the world, listen up: Don't bet against me. You'll lose. In the words of Muhammad Ali, "If you even dream of beating me you better wake up and APOLOGIZE."